The Enduring Ripples of War

The Enduring Ripples of War

Published by The Conrad Press in the United Kingdom 2019

Tel: +44(0)1227 472 874
www.theconradpress.com
info@theconradpress.com

ISBN 978-1-911546-76-4

Typesetting and Cover Design by:
Charlotte Mouncey, www.bookstyle.co.uk

The Conrad Press logo was designed by Maria Priestley.

Printed and bound in Great Britain
by Clays Ltd, Elcograf S.p.A.

The Enduring Ripples of War

Kathryn Cowling

For my beautiful daughters, Leigh and Emily, they have made me the person I am today.

I

GERMANY
November 12 1930
LEONARD ROSENTHAL

I stood just outside the living-room door listening to Phineas, my father, and Hana, my mother, as they sat discussing their worries about what was happening in our home country, Germany. They didn't know I was there. I heard my father sigh as he recalled how bad the persecution of Jewish people had been; in the past. He hoped that now we lived in more enlightened times, the oppression would cease, but with the election of a new chancellor; that was becoming increasingly unlikely.

I didn't tell my parents because I thought they had enough to worry about, but I was frightened too. Life was rapidly turning into a living nightmare. Our neighbours and people who we thought of as friends spat in our faces as we walked past them down the street where we'd lived happily all our lives. We had known these people for many years and they'd frequented our little pawn shop on many occasions.

Our family had shared the trials of their lives with them, celebrated their births and mourned their deaths. Father often helped out some of our customers financially; if they were struggling, and he was happy to do this if he could. He told me many times that, in his view, that's what friends were for. Now these people had turned on us and, for, seemingly, no reason at all, began to treat us as though we were rabid dogs at all.

I heard, through the gossip at my village school, how some of the Jewish people living in the big cities were suffering physical abuse on a regular basis and I was frightened that it would be our turn next. I didn't want to believe that the townsfolk who I'd known and cared about all my life could be so cruel but they were. Some of our closest friends began to hiss vile names when I passed them on my way to or from school and sometimes they shoved me to the ground.

Many of our German friends and neighbours turned a blind eye. The new chancellor seemed, at first, to be an asset to our country, but now things had taken a chilling turn. He talked about building a country with a master race of blue-eyed blonde-haired people. Germany was no longer a safe place to live in, and we knew the situation would get worse as long as this man was in power.

My father had a brother and sister-in-law who ran a bakery in a little village some twenty miles from us. They'd written to tell us that they'd had bricks thrown through their shop windows and the words 'filthy Jews' painted across their front door. They were hopeful the situation would improve as they didn't want to leave the country they loved; my father and I were not optimistic. The needless violence seemed to be spiralling out of control, and we were powerless to stop it.

My uncle went onto tell us that they were relieved that their only daughter Gerta now lived in Ireland and was safe. The ultimate idea was for me and my family to join her but, unfortunately, my father had lost touch over the years, and he was desperately trying to find her exact whereabouts. He believed our lives depended on it, and I thought he was right. Germany was becoming more unsafe for any person of Jewish origin who stilled remained in the country.

I heard my parents discuss how utterly terrified they were as they sat, talking in whispered tones, about their plans for our family. As I eaves-dropped, I still felt as though it didn't seem possible that our lives had turned into this hideous nightmare in such a short time. I'd lived in Germany all my life and regarded it my patriotic home. My parents tried to shelter us two boys from what was happening, but they couldn't hide the harsh reality.

My younger brother, Maciej, had just turned eleven-years-old and was an anxious, sensitive boy, so I could understand my parents wanting to keep him ignorant of the situation. It would terrify the poor child, and that would be of no help to anyone. I, however, was twelve–and-a half years old and carried a much older head on my shoulders, so I felt a little annoyed that my parents had not seen fit to include me in their plans for our future survival. Nevertheless, it was not my place to question what my father had decided, and this was how I came to be loitering outside half-open doors trying to listen to how we would all escape to Ireland.

I strained my ears to listen as my father outlined his plans to my mother. I imagined their tired eyes in the flickering candlelight. My father explained that his eventual plan was for us to travel across Germany until we reached the border to France, then cross over in whatever way we could and then, travel through France and ultimately get a boat over the channel into England. My parent's pawn shop was small but profitable. It enabled my parents to make an adequate living, but little money was left over, so trying to save money for our escape would take many months. This frustrated me because I believed the sooner we could leave the better it would be.

I knew my father would also have preferred us to flee straight away, but we would have to wait until enough funds had been saved for the hazardous journey. My mother fed the family as cheaply as she could and mended clothes many times over to enable money to be squirrelled into the small, metal strong box that would pay for the journey. The box also contained a map of our escape route. Mother and father pored over the plan many times to decipher the quickest and safest route possible.

Gerta played a key part in our escape, as Ireland, was the place in which we hoped to make our home. Father had told me how he'd written to the Red Cross to ask them for help in locating the cousin he'd not seen for many years. The only information he'd managed to ascertain was that Gerta had married an Irish man, named Pat Coleman, when she was seventeen years old and moved to her new husband's native country. If we could make contact with her then she may be able to provide a safe haven for our small family.

I managed to get a part-time job delivering groceries for our local shop, and soon, even Maciej was earning money by running errands for the local traders. Father had explained to Maciej that we were to leave as soon as possible, but he'd not told them him the reason so as not to frighten him. I knew exactly how perilous our existence was and was aware of the importance of a swift escape. I encouraged Maciej to work and make as much money as he could on the pretence that we could save up for a new bicycle and that thought spurred him on nicely.

Over half a million Jews lived in Germany, and both my father and mother had pondered many times as to why the oppression of the Jewish people reoccurred throughout history. My mother listened as my father ranted about being unable to understand how a human being could turn on his fellow man for no determinable reason. I vehemently agreed with him. We both longed for our family to exist in a life without fear. The only way to achieve that aim was by moving away from the place where we'd had lived for many years and which we thought of as home.

2

One night, all of us, mother, father, Maciej and I, were in the little flat above the pawn shop sleeping peacefully. I remember feeling safe and warm and comfortably cocooned in my bed. At first, the sounds of smashing glass didn't register, but finally it made its way into my unconscious mind, and brought instantly awake.

Throwing my bedclothes aside, I walked towards my small bedroom window that overlooked the street and was terrified to see a rabble of men and young boys outside. I recognised them as school friends and neighbours, but their faces were twisted in a mask of hatred and bloodlust.

I watched as the crowd stood in front the house of my elderly schoolmaster, who lived across the street from us. One by one, they smashed every window at the front of his property. They then smashed down the front door and, they pulled the old man and his hysterical wife out onto the street in their nightclothes. I could hardly believe what I was seeing. The baying mob callously set fire to the house as the occupants watched helplessly. I watched, hid behind the curtain, paralysed with shock and incredulity.

The group of men then began to beat the schoolmaster and his wife tried to protect him. Every instinct in my body screamed at me to help the couple but I was frozen with fear and unable to properly comprehend what was happening. Somewhere in the house, I heard my father telling my mother to rise quickly, dress and pack a few belongings.

He then shouted out to me and Maciej, repeating the same words, adding that we must put our belongings in our school satchels. I shook myself into action, still in a state of shock and bewilderment. I did as I was told, then strode into the living room and watched as my father grabbed the tin box from the back of the sideboard drawer. He'd shown it to me several times over the past couple of years and had talked me through the journey we'd be taking.

Once we were all ready for the outdoors, my father silently mouthed for us to follow him quietly down the narrow stairway at the back of the shop and out into the small alley behind. The little lane was unlit, and we felt our way along the wall in pitch darkness. The four of us stealthily and soundlessly walked away from the only home I'd ever known. I could tell Maciej, was terrified, because he was trembling. He whispered to me that he thought the German people would be able to hear the thudding of his heart and that we would be caught. I patted his shoulder and pushed him onwards.

We listened, with terrified awareness, as the sounds of violence and destruction followed our every step. As we neared the end of the alleyway and turned a sharp corner, we felt a great relief to be moving away from the volatile situation. However, without warning, a figure appeared in front of us causing us to stop in our tracks.

Whoever it was had hidden himself in a doorway but now stood barring our escape. A small crescent moon lit up his face and I moved closer, recognising the person as a man who'd been coming to my father's shop for many years. I held onto Maciej and watched as Father begged him to allow us to pass. He pleaded for the lives of mother, Maciej and I. He grabbed the man's hands and offered him money or the keys to the Pawn shop.

The man laughed, shook his head from side to side and steadfastly refused. He drew a whistle from his pocket, placed it between his lips, and emitted a loud shrieking sound, alerting the enemy to our location. His cold, gaze bore down onto the two of us, and Maciej began to tremble more violently. Suddenly, my father hurled himself at the man and flung him to the floor as the shouting, frenzied gang turned towards the shrill sound.

As they fought, my mother lunged forward to try and protect my father from the blows that his attacker was now raining down on him. In the doorway where the man stood was a large rock which my mother leant down and picked it up. She then used the whole weight of her body to lunge forward and smash it into the back of the assailant's head as he straddled Father and punched him again and again.

The attacker groaned with pain then fell to the side of my father's body, with blood pouring from the head wound. Father struggled to his feet. His eyes were bloodied and swollen and blood trickled from his nose. He quickly ripped a small key from a chain around his neck and thrust this into my hands along with the tin box.

He ordered me, mother and Maciej to flee away, as fast as our feet would take us, and not to look back. Mother steadfastly refused and neither myself, nor Maciej, moved. My father became angry and shouted at us to go and pushed us roughly away as the mob began to sound terrifyingly nearer.

I mentally shook myself out of my stupor, the fear of the approaching men quickening my thinking; I kissed my mother hurriedly and patted my father affectionately on the shoulder before grabbing Maciej's hand and running as fast as I could away from the danger. The terror made me feel as though I couldn't breathe. I expected to be caught at any moment and prayed to God to keep us safe.

As we turned left, the lane tapered lane into another small alley, I briefly turned backwards for one last look at my parents. I watched, horrified, as my father was being pummelled to the ground by at least six men and my mother's clothes were ripped off her back. This gave wings to my already speedy feet and I quickly sprinted away from the terrible sight, all the time urging my younger brother to run and never stop. I knew I would never forget the look of utter fear on my mother's face as long as I lived nor would I ever rid myself of the sense of guilt I felt leaving her there.

3

I had only ever known life in an institution. I was told that I was illegitimate and that my mother had died in childbirth. That was the only knowledge of any family, I was given. The orphanage where I was raised gave no comfort or love to the tiny inmates. The food was bland and never seemed to supress the hunger that gnawed at my stomach constantly. I didn't miss having a family because I had never known the joy of living amongst one.

I never ever possessed one single new article of clothing in my whole life. Every item, including my pants was either handed down or donated. Some children who lived at the home with me were lucky enough to get adopted. This didn't happen to me because staff always informed any would-be parents that I was a trouble- maker and to give me a wide berth. I disagreed with their opinion but who would take any notice of me?

In truth, I didn't go looking for trouble; I just expressed my opinion, whenever I thought necessary. I was told consistently told, by anyone in authority, that I must be seen and not heard. Never, throughout my childhood, could I work out why I was not allowed to ask for warmer clothes or extra food so I continued to do so.

When I did request these things, I spent many of my younger years being 'punished' by being locked in the dingy, dark cellar for hours at a time. I was also disciplined for asking questions, like why we had to go to bed when it was still light outside. I really didn't mind, though, being in the cellar, I was not afraid of the dark and it gave me time to think. The cellar had and earthy, musky smell that, to me, seemed more homely than the disinfectant-like smell that lingered all about the children's home where I lived.

All of us were taken to church each Sunday and we all had our own bible. I had no Sunday 'best' clothes but the girls were allowed to wear a hat, if we possessed one, or a coloured ribbon, I had neither. In the afternoons, all the orphans attended Sunday school and, when I turned twelve years old, was instructed to attend bible studies with the priest.

I was very much looking forward to this as it would be something different in my humdrum, ordered life. But, sadly, once I had attended two or three times, I found these lessons boring. This being the case, I was quite happy when I was summoned to the priest's sitting room, in the middle of one such lesson. Once there the kindly man offered me a glass of milk and a biscuit. I was overjoyed; biscuits, for me, were a rare and exciting luxury.

Once I had eaten it, however, the priest insisted I thank him, which I already had done. When I questioned how I could thank him anymore, he shoved his warm, sweaty hands down the front of my dress and touched my small budding breasts.

Feeling a mixture of shocked and disgust, I pulled his hands out of my clothing and fled the room. The next Sunday when I was invited into the sitting room my mind was in turmoil.

I longed for a biscuit and a glass of milk but I didn't want the horrible man touching me again. In the end, my hunger won and I walked into the warm, comfy room and drank my milk and slowly ate the biscuit leisurely so that the taste would remain with me for a while.

This time, when the man in his long dark gown and white, stiff collar approached, I was ready for him and darted nimbly to the door. To my horror, I found it bolted; before I could unlock it, my assailant was upon me. His sweeping black robe reminded me of a black buzzard circling its prey. The kindly smile was now gone and his eyes seemed to have turned black. The priest pushed me to the floor and put his hand up my skirt. I was a slightly built little girl and my attacker was an obese, well fed man.

As I struggled to escape, to my absolute horror, I felt his podgy fingers inside my pants. I frantically tried to think what I could do to stop him. I remembered, some time ago in the playground, when one of the boys had been hit in the groin with a cricket ball and he rolled around writhing in agony. Someone had told me that the ball had hit his 'private parts' and that would really hurt.

Quickly I tried to calculate where the 'private parts' of the priest's body were. It was difficult because his body was swamped by his enormous vestal robe. I aimed a sharp kick in the direction that I felt would hurt. I must have hit the spot because the priest went flying backwards and rolled around like the boy in the playground, holding his crotch and screaming at the top of his voice.

I inwardly congratulated myself then quickly scrambled up, unbolted the door and fled into the matron's office at top speed;

I banged on the door and heard her shout 'come'. I hurtled through the door and once I had got my breath back, I began to explain to matron what had happened.

I was already trembling uncontrollably and was shocked to the core when the woman I had run to for help, slapped my face so hard that it felt like a bee stung me. I was then dragged, by the hair, to the punishment cellar where I was forced to stay for two days with nothing to eat or drink.

When I was finally freed from my prison, the dim light of the corridor almost blinded me as I had spent so much time in total darkness. The next morning, during assembly, I was hoisted up to the front of the room. I looked down at the curious faces of my fellow orphans. The congregation of children were told about my wickedness and how I had deliberately hurt the gentle priest when he had only shown me kindness.

Typically, I interrupted matron to say he had not shown much kindness when he put his hand in my knickers. This earned me another day's punishment but I wasn't bothered. So far, for all of my life, I had been told how grateful and unquestioning I should be and that I must never speak until I was spoken to. To my mind, they could deprive me of food, drink and clothing but they could not stop me talking when I wanted to.

The next day, back in the long dormitory which I shared with eleven other girls, my friend Jean, asked me if I was alright in a whispering voice, once the lights had been turned out. I replied that I was fine and didn't care about being punished. Small, mousy Jean told me that I was brave for speaking out and that she would be much too scared to, I whispered back:

'Jean, if the priest invites you into his office for a glass of milk and a biscuit, say no, it doesn't matter how hungry you, he's a horrible man who only wants to hurt you, no matter what everyone else says,' Jean sighed:

'I'd love a glass of milk and biscuit even if he is a horrible man,' Jean answered dreamily.

'Promise me Jean!' I hissed as loud as I could without being told off for talking.

'Alright,' Jean answered, sounding thoroughly depressed and upset but I couldn't help it, I needed to be sure that she was aware of the danger of being alone with the so called 'holy man'.

I tiptoed out of my bed and walked over to where Jean lay. I kissed her on the cheek because I didn't want her to think I was angry with her. I then said goodnight to her and pulled her blanket up to her chin. I climbed back into my own bed and lay staring into the darkness.

I tried not to worry but I thought, if Jean didn't speak up for herself more, she wouldn't get very far in life. She would be no match against the dreadful priest and I really hoped that she would listen to me and not let her hunger get the better of her. I, however, intended to make a better life for myself as soon as I was free of the orphanage. I longed to be self-sufficient and reliant on no one. I think Jean was one of those people who would always need someone else to take care of her and I wished I change her outlook on life.

When I reached fourteen years old, the elders at the orphanage found me a job working in a wool shop. I truly believe they couldn't wait to see the back of me. The shop was owned by an elderly lady, Mrs King who was a kind, caring lady who treated me so much better than I had ever been treated before. Mrs King instructed me on what to do in the little shop. She told me what wools were kept where, all the orders that had been placed and a thousand other little jobs that kept me happily busy.

Before long, I was virtually running the business single handed. This was because Mrs King spent more and more time in the sitting room behind the shop, caring for her husband who was bed-ridden. I didn't mind, I loved my work. Mrs King had a daughter, Mary, but she lived down in Cornwall. They kept in touch by letter and Mrs King often showed me what she had written. Mary wrote how she was always grateful to me for the help I gave her aging parents. I grew to love the lovely old couple more each day and would gladly have worked there for nothing if I didn't need the money to survive.

I remained living at the orphanage because this enabled me to save as much money as I could. Legally, I was allowed to remain there until I was sixteen, and then I would be sent out into the world to tackle life on my own. I hated staying at the orphanage but it was the only way I would be able to save enough money to find a home of my own. The authorities ensured the orphanage paid for my upkeep until I was officially classed as an adult. I thought they owed me that much at the very least. I felt the happiest I had been for my entire life and began to joyously plan my future, away from the orphanage.

4

August 25 1932
Gerta Rosenthal

I sat in my tiny cottage in Donegal, Ireland, warming my sore, work-worn hands with a cup of tea. They were red and dry and looked a lot older than they actually were. I had moved to Donegal in Ireland with my new husband nearly sixteen years earlier. Pat had come to Germany with his family where his father had a job. I was just sixteen when he walked into the bakery that my parents owned, to buy some pastries for his family. I was working behind the counter, on that particular day, and was immediately smitten.

I knew, however, that Pat, who spoke fluent German with a soft hint of an Irish accent, would never look at me. I had a large, Jewish nose, the same as my mother had. In my mother's case, however, her lips were full, her face was rounded and her skin was like porcelain, so this softened her nose. My features were sharp and unforgiving. In my mind, only my vibrant green eyes saved me from being totally ugly. So, I was just happy to see Pat most days, to serve him, chat with him and admire him from afar.

I was well aware that my mother and father watched with hidden amusement at my infatuation for the young Irish man. I was their only child and they intended for me to marry a Jewish man and practise the Jewish faith. I however knew right then and there that I would never love anyone but Pat. It didn't matter that he didn't love me, just to see his handsome face every day was all I needed. It made my world was complete.

On one particular day, I was in the shop alone. Pat had been coming to the bakery regularly for the last three or four months. My mother was baking in the kitchen at the back and my father was out buying supplies and visiting his cousin Phineas who lived in the city, some miles away with his wife, Hana and two young sons. I had not seen Phineas for many years but always remembered him because he had stuck up for me when I was a child and a spiteful boy had called me Pinocchio, in reference to my large nose. Next time my father visited I meant to go along as well.

The shop bell clanged loudly, and I raised my eyes to see the thin, wiry body of Pat walking towards the counter. As always, he took my breath away. His blonde hair was unruly and hung over one of his eyes, which were small but bright blue. His thin lips smiled at me as he asked how I was, as he did every day, and I told him that I was fine and happy to see him once more. Today, however, he also asked if I would like to go to the cinema with him.

At first I was dumbstruck, and could hardly believe my ears, then I quickly stuttered a yes, and our romance began. At eighteen Pat Coleman was two years old than me. When, two years later, he announced that his family were to return to Ireland, I was heartbroken until he explained that he would like me to accompany him, as his wife.

This caused major ructions in the Rosenthal household. My parents begged me to stay then forbade me to see Pat again.

It was only when I threatened to run away that they finally relented and begrudgingly gave us their blessing. We were hastily married in a small ceremony attended by a tiny gathering of our close families. The marriage would enable me to travel to Ireland with Pat and his family.

I stood on the deck of the ship just six weeks later and watched as it approached the land that would become my home. As the boat sailed into the Irish port I was immediately taken with this beautiful island. The ocean was emerald green and shone like glass as sea birds soared in the skies above. I smiled with happiness as I looked at the vision before me. The land was awash with lush with thick greenery and enormous trees with roots that spread across the ground like reedy, gnarled fingers.

When we first arrived, we lived with Pat's parents until finally we found a cottage to rent in a tiny hamlet to the south of the island. Our neighbours, the Logans, were older than the two of us but Pat and I soon became good friends with the couple. When the Logan's daughter, Lucy was born, when Elsie Logan was nearly forty two years old, no one was more overjoyed for them than Pat and I. Life, I conceded, was wonderful and I patiently waited to become pregnant with my own child, only for tragedy to strike far too early in our fledgling marriage.

When I finally became pregnant Pat was the proudest man on earth. He worked for a company that made wooden furniture and loved his job. A lot of the furniture in our tiny cottage had been made by Pat and I was very proud of him. Life was blissful and I considered myself very lucky until tragedy struck. In the sixth month of my pregnancy I began to suffer great pain and staggered next door to the Logan household to beg for help. Elsie helped me to a chair whilst her husband grabbed his bicycle and rode off at speed to get the village doctor.

As he pedalled furiously, he spotted a workmate of Pat's and stopped to ask him if he would inform the father-to-be of what was happening as soon as he could. The man immediately understood as he knew, as did the rest of the close- knit village, that the baby was not due for a couple of months and sprinted off to find Pat. Mr Logan returned with the doctor and found me in an advanced state of labour and in great distress as I knew my baby was coming too early.

I cried and begged the doctor to save my child. The poor man tried his best but to no avail. The baby arrived but mine and Pats tiny son was stillborn. I truly felt as though my heart would break. My wonderful, joyous life had been shattered in am a matter of hours and now I had to tell Pat that his tiny son was dead and had never taken a breath in this world. I was inconsolable and the distress I felt shook my whole body and I thought my tears would never dry.

I watched out of the tiny bedroom window as the doctor left my house. I had never felt so empty or alone in my entire life. A sudden movement caught my eye and I strained to look out at a distraught man haring up the hill towards my home. I didn't know what he was saying but I was to learn very soon and that news nearly finished me off. I truly wanted my world to end.

The man explained to the doctor that there had been an accident and a pile of logs had become loose and fallen on Pat. Pat was dead. The doctor turned and re-entered the property he had just left. He had the unenviable job of telling me that, not only had I lost my child, but that my husband was dead also. I prayed for God to allow me to join Pat and my son but it was not to be. I was destined to be alone and the only happiness I found would be in my memories.

5

GERMANY
August 25 1932
LEONARD ROSENTHAL

I was desperately dragging Maciej behind me imploring him to keep up. I could hear his strangled sobs but I knew had to keep running, there was no time for me to turn and pacify him. My throat burned and I found it almost impossible to breathe but still I ran. Maciej wept pitifully as I held tightly onto his wrist and pulled him almost off his feet. Soon, the houses started to peter out as we reached the outskirts of the town. We ran down a narrow track that I knew would lead us into the dense forest. We had played in this area many times.

This was before our normal life disintegrated and madness threw everything we had ever known far out of our reach. Both of us leapt over a hedge, simultaneously, in order to lose ourselves among the large spruces. Maciej finally seemed to grasp the urgency of the situation and stopped his whimpering. We came across a massive tree trunk; we had made a den inside it, a few months previously so I knew it would make a good hiding place. I crawled inside and Maciej followed.

Once we were safely inside the bowel of the tree, we covered ourselves with dry leaves and foliage to hide from whoever may be chasing us. After a short time we heard the sound of approaching footsteps and Maciej began, once again, to whimper. I pressed my hand across my younger brother's mouth and gave him a penetrating stare, warning him to be quiet. Then, the noises of feet stamping around undergrowth sent a poisonous chill coursing through my very soul. I heard the voice of my school friend, Nicolai, speak:

'Where are you Rosenthals? ' he growled, we Germans do not like filthy Jews so you better show yourselves before we find you.'

This felt to me like a very strange thing to say because, only two days before, Nicolai and, I along with some other boys that lived in our road, had played football in the street in front of his house while Maciej and Nicolai's younger sister, Marta sat at their kitchen table colouring in and sharing crayons. The speed at which the people I once considered my friends turned into deadly enemies terrified and shocked me.

Maciej and I sat still as statues, hardly daring to breathe. I felt nauseous with a raging terror that thudded through my whole body. After a few minutes, which seemed much longer, our old school friends became bored and I heard the terrifying footsteps tramping away, back through the forest. We sat for what seemed like hours but, was probably, no more than one, before eventually stirring from our hiding place and looking tentatively around.

After double checking that there was no one else around I was satisfied that the coast was clear. We both emerged from the safety of the tree trunk. I was shaken to the core and Maciej looked as though he was in a state of utter shock. His face was devoid of colour and his eyes were red rimmed with crying. My heart went out to my little brother and I pulled him close and hugged him tightly. I so wanted to take away his pain and fear but felt helpless to offer him any comfort.

I finally released him and explained that we had to get away as fast as we could. It was what our parents wanted. Maciej sniffed and nodded and I told him that he was a good boy and Father would be proud of him. We then began our hazardous journey to safety, clutching the precious tin box that my father had thrust into my unwillingly hands. Maciej and I continued to walk through the night until the dawn broke and we were both exhausted. Finally, we stumbled upon the deserted remains of a derelict house and stepped inside.

Once I determined it was uninhabited and safe, we both lay down on the hard floor and immediately fell into a restless sleep. It did not matter that the cold concrete of the floor penetrated through my clothes. The extreme fear and sheer exhaustion I felt made my body to shut down and sleep overwhelmed me.

I finally woke just as evening was approaching once more. Edging myself away from my sleeping brother I went out to see if there was anything about that I could use to light a fire with. As it had been a dry August, I found plenty of twigs and set about building a fire, the way my father had taught me to do many years earlier.

From the leather satchels we carried with us, I took out some of the food my mother had packed and shook Maciej awake. I felt so sorry for my younger brother. His bewilderment was almost palpable and his young face was devoid of colour. I held his hand and promised him I would take care of him. My words did not seem to penetrate through to him, and his eyes stared straight ahead, as though he was looking at some unknown entity. I guessed that he was in shock and decided I must give him time to recover and be there for him when and if he needed me.

We both sat eating in the fire light, neither of us speaking. I think we were both in a state of silent astonishment from what had happened to our family in such a short period of time. One minute life was the normal routine. We went to school, worked and played with our neighbours and the next we were running like fugitives from enemies that were once our friends.

I tried not to think about what had happened to my parents. I wanted to pretend that they had escaped and would eventually catch up with us but in my mind, I knew this could not be true and my heart broke when I thought of the courageous sacrifice they had made to give us our freedom. To make they're detriment worthwhile I knew that I had to get my brother and myself to safety. That was what my parents wanted and I would do everything in my power to give them their wish.

Once we had both drank a little water, I opened the tin box that my father had earlier thrust into my unwilling hands. Inside was a map of the journey that my father was hoping we would all undertake, some money, my father's watch and both my parent's wedding rings. Also, there was a small black and white photo of our family in happier times.

I touched it gently and softly rubbed my finger over my parents smiling faces, wishing we were back in that moment and everything that had happened was a terrifying dream. There was also a letter from the Red Cross who had written to say that they had been trying to locate Gerta Rosenthal. It stated that they were certain that she was in Donegal, Ireland and was now Gerta Coleman.

They had forwarded her the letter that my Father had sent and hoped that she would receive it sometime in the future. This gave me a tiny iota of hope. We now had one relative and we knew her name and roughly her whereabouts. After a small rest, we doused the small fire and continued our voyage following our father's precious map. It was difficult to keep the tears at bay every time I looked at the map. I imagined my father leaning over it, his eyes straining in the candle light, trying to ensure it would lead us all to safety.

I swore to myself I would never forget my parents and if we were lucky enough to escape with our lives, I would search for them and try and find out what happened to them. Even if my search only produced gravestones with their names etched on, it would give me some kind of closure.

All of us Rosenthal's were of Jewish ancestry, although we did not practise any particular religion and regarded ourselves as German citizens. This made the persecution of my family very hard to take but I could not allow myself to dwell on bitter thoughts and anger. I had to make it my priority to get myself and Maciej as far away from our home as possible.

Before the world descended into madness, if the weather was fine, every Sunday our whole family would all head for the countryside with a picnic, packed by our mother, and just enjoy being out in the fresh air.

I was lucky; these weekly excursions meant that I was familiar with the beginning of the route we would need to take as it covered this area. I decided that we would sleep during the day and continue our journey at night; I felt it would be safer that way as we were less likely to be spotted in darkness. In reality

I had no idea which would be the safer option and could only use my instincts.

We passed many small farms where we bought food and if too many questions were asked by the German land owners, I would explain, laughingly, that we were 'bunking off' school and having an adventure. The fact we had our school satchels with us, added credence to the lie. If anyone questioned further, I explained that we were called Heinz and Franz Schneider and that we would be heading back home before dark. This seemed to satisfy any further enquiries asked and we continued with our journey.

The voyage was long and hard, especially when we left the unfamiliar territory and had to follow the map that my father had drawn. Luckily my wonderful father had sketched in great detail. The plan was to cross the border into France and try to secure a lift with local fishermen across the channel to England. Once there, we would travel to Liverpool and visit the dock office to see if they had received any form of communication from Gerta Coleman.

Both of us were bewildered and frightened, but I did my best to hide this from Maciej, as we fled through Germany and hopefully onto freedom. Any unexplained shadows sent daggers of fear stabbing at my body. If we saw any strangers we immediately hid. Not knowing who was a friend or a foe was one of the hardest parts, I trusted no one and avoided as much contact with the human race as we could.

It took many months for Maciej and me to travel through Germany and Belgium, then finally cross the border into France. We were both dirty and dishevelled and had sold almost everything we owned in order to feed ourselves. We had turned into two feral type animals that didn't wash enough and foraged for food like ancient hunters. Our clothes were ragged and torn and our shoes had holes in the soles. We both became immune to the discomforts we suffered and kept our minds fixed on our eventual destination.

The two young boys who had fled from the baying mob many months ago, now, no longer existed; our childish innocence had gone along with our past family life. We had been forced to grow up very quickly in order to survive the ordeal we found ourselves in. We had sold most of our possessions along the way to get money for food. The only thing we had left to sell was our fathers watch and this was what we hoped would pay for our passage to England. We went hungry for the final few days of our journey to ensure we held onto our remaining precious possession.

We reached Calais very early on a misty January morning. At first, to me, it looked like a mirage. We had been travelling for so long I was never really sure if we would make it but we had and I was a little frightened what would happen to us next. The port was busy and there was several fishing vessels moored alongside each other. These varied in size and age. We lay down to hide while I surveyed the boats and tried to surmise which one may be willing to take us across the channel.

My heart was pounding with fear as I approached the nearest fishing boat I saw. It looked like an old boat. The outside paint was peeling off and barnacles clung to its base and climbed up the sides. I eyed all crafts of all sizes lined up alongside the dock. My distrust of my fellow man made me hesitate to ask for help but I knew we had to cross the channel and we could not do it on our own.

I told Maciej to stay where he was, just out of sight of any of the French fisherman. Taking a deep breath and walking with a confidence I did not possess, I approached the first boat I came across. It was a smallish vessel with the name '*Orage*' painted on it port side. I walked forward and spoke to an elderly man who was hoisting some nets aboard. There were no other men on board the boat; he was a lone angler who struggled with the work he had to do. His aging fingers were gnarled and bent and he winced with pain every time he picked anything up.

I touched his shoulder and he turned to face me and I began to speak to him, I asked if he would take us over to England and showed him the watch that would be payment for our passage. Thankfully, he seemed to understand my stilted English. I could speak no French at all and wished I'd listened more carefully when my mother had tried to teach me to speak the English language. He turned and looked me up and down. His face was deeply lined and tanned from many years out on the open sea but he had kind looking eyes.

I tried to smile at him bit my nervousness would not allow me to. I waited for what seemed a very long time but in reality was no time at all. The fisherman muttered '*non*' then lifted his hand and if to sweep me out the way as if I was some tiresome moth flapping around his face. I was bitterly disappointed and had to swallow my tears but I thanked him and turned to walk towards the next boat.

This crew also refused to take us across the channel and so I carried on asking every fisherman I could see but no one was willing to take us to England. The frustration I felt was tearing at my stomach. I could actually see the distant banks of England from where I stood; we were so close to safety but also so far. After several fruitless attempts to get a lift across the water I headed back to where I had left Maciej hiding. I couldn't stop myself.

I knelt down and cried bitterly, I allowed my tears to fall unhindered. Everything was so unfair. We had committed no crime, yet here we were, homeless and hungry and trapped in a country that hated us. I felt Maciej's arm around my shoulder and I put my hand on his. My whole body sagged with exhaustion and my inability to get us to safety felt like a physical pain jabbing at my chest:

'It's no use mate, no one will take us,' I sobbed.

Maciej sat down beside me. We had travelled so far and now it looked like it had all been for nothing and the strain was too much to bear. I briefly wandered if we could swim the channel then dismissed this thought almost right away. At that moment in time I wished I had a gun. I wanted to shoot myself and my brother, at least everything would all be over for us and we would no longer have to fight anymore.

I'm not sure how long the two of us sat there in a state of total dejection and misery but at some point I felt as though I was being watched and so I raised my head. A few feet away I saw the elderly fisherman who was the first one I had asked for help earlier that day. As he approached I looked up into his old eyes. I was afraid, I didn't know if he had reported us to the authorities even though we had done nothing wrong. His voice was so quiet that, at first, I barely heard what he said until he repeated it once more:

'Come,' he said and indicated we should follow him. I scuttled to my feet and pulled my brother behind me. I wanted to believe that this man was helping us but I still had my doubts and looked constantly around to see if there was anyone coming for us.

At the same time, I quickly followed the man to his boat. All the other vessels were now out at sea and this was the only one left in port. The man pointed inside the boat and we clambered in. The fisherman picked up a tarpaulin and indicated that we both crawl underneath it.

I was a little worried about exactly what his plans were but I had little choice but to obey, all our options had been exhausted; we had to do as we were told. I pulled Maciej under the cloth and pulled it over our heads so that we could not be seen. I heard the anchor being wound up. The boat listed a little as it sailed into against the tide then it was calm. The only sound was of the soft waves pushing against the outside of the boat. With each passing minute I silently begged God or anyone who was listening to help us. I prayed we were being taken to protection and the man was not working for the German Nazis.

Finally the boat came to a halt, around five or six hours later; I remained lying as still as I could with one arm over Maciej. I swear my heavy breathing could be heard for miles around and the terror I felt matched the same fear as when I ran from the mob that attacked my parents. I knew that this was the end of the line. We had either reached safety or we had been handed over to our enemies.

The tarpaulin was suddenly lifted and the daylight stung my eyes. The man stood and offered me his hand. He helped into a standing position then pointed to the side of the boat. I felt stiff and my legs ached at being immobilised for such a long time in a cramped space. Ignoring my discomfort I pulled

Maciej to his feet and looked around.

To my utter untold relief and tear-filled joy I realised that we had crossed the channel and were in England. The anchor was dropped and the vessel was moored. It was hidden by tall cliffs that surrounded a tiny crag. A smidgen of golden yellow sand led upwards in the direction of the cliffs. Further on was a steep and precarious looking path, winding its way upwards, which led to a grassy mound at the clifftop.

I grabbed the old man's hand and shook it while thanking him profusely at the same time. Tears of relief poured down my face and I didn't care, we had made it. Our rescuer stepped off the boat and we both followed. On land, he pointed to the narrow pathway between the two cliffs and said we must follow it to the top then head west.

I nodded then took my father's watch from my pocket and offered it to the man, who was now my saviour. He shook his head and refused to take the watch. He then handed me some cheese and bread, wrapped in a grubby muslin cloth and a bottle of water.

The lump that formed in my throat was so big that it threatened to choke me. I handed the food and water to my brother and hugged the man as tightly as I could. As we pulled apart there were tears in both our eyes. The kindly fisherman then climbed back aboard his craft and headed out to sea. I would never forget our liberator as long as I lived.

I didn't think I'd ever be as grateful to anyone in my whole life as I was to the stranger who cared enough and risked his own life to take us to safety. I waved until he was out of sight. Maciej and I had been too afraid to reveal our true identities in case the friendly angler turned on us, as our friends in Germany had. Too late, I realised he was a true friend and hoped we would meet again in a more peaceful time so I could thank him properly and tell him our real names.

It was such an enormous relief to feel my feet walking on British soil and both Maciej and I smiled widely at each other. This was an action that had been alien to us for so long now that it felt strange to feel my lips stretched into a grin. I hoped my father would be proud if he could see us now, safely in England. I shook myself back to the present time and back to practicalities that now faced us.

We now needed to make our way to Liverpool, first we had to find a ferry to sail to Ireland and hopefully find Gerta Coleman. She was the only person who could help us. Although I was daunted by the journey ahead, I was no longer afraid. My father had told me that the English people had no hatred for the Jews and would take care of us and even welcome us to their country. I wished that we didn't look so dishevelled and ragged. I didn't want us to be mistaken for thieves or vagabonds but there was not a lot I could do about our outward appearance.

Once we had scrambled up the cliff and walked the few miles to the nearest town, I pawned my father's watch. I hoped with all my heart that I would be able to retrieve it again sometime in the future. But at this time we needed the money more than the watch. We now had our fare to Liverpool. This was where my father had sent the telegram onto Gerta many months before. As the train trundled nearer to our destination, I felt my body physically relax. I had not been aware of how tense I had been for the last hellish months.

The train finally trundled into the main station in the

middle of Liverpool. We both stepped down the steps and onto the grey platform that was teeming with people rushing about, heading for their destination. It was not dissimilar from Germany's main station in the layout and style. The main difference was the signage which was all in English. Once we were out outside, I was a little unsure of where to head for next. I knew we would need to get a ferry over to Ireland but I had no idea what direction to go in.

I managed to speak enough English to ask an elderly lady which direction we needed to go. She explained slowly, so that I could understand. She said it was a long journey but pointed us in the direction we needed to go. We began on our trek, both buoyed up by the feeling that we were getting closer to cousin Gerta and sanctuary.

We slept anywhere that we could find, at night, which was warm and begged for food from anyone we met along the way. We finally reached the telegram office where we hoped we would find a letter waiting for us but were disappointed to find, on our arrival, there was nothing. All we could do was wait and hope that at Some point Gerta would write to us and tell us where she lived.

Each day we awoke from our rough sleeping place we headed for the telegram office, hopeful for news from Gerta. For three and half long weeks, there was no news and for the second time, since our flight had begun, I began to lose hope. I had no idea what to do if we didn't hear from our cousin. I knew that there were orphanages we could go to because my father had talked about them. He had explained that it was best to go there if, at any time, our family became separated. These places tended to split families up and my father wanted to ensure that

Maciej and I stayed together. But if that was our only option, that is what I would do.

I didn't want us to have to enter into an institution but I was becomingly increasingly desperate and hungry and wasn't sure how long my brother and I could continue living he way we were. The nights were cold and some days we went without food. I wrestled with my conscience. I needed to consider Maciej's welfare but also my father's wishes.

I decided to give it another couple of more days to see if our relative would contact us, if not I would have to go to someone for help. I was loathe to do this but our options were running out and Maciej had developed a hacking cough due to us sleeping outside and not getting the necessary food and drink for our survival.

On the first day of the fourth week, we entered the office and were again disappointed when we were told that no telegram had arrived. I knew that I could not subject my brother to one more night sleeping outside. He was ill and sallow looking and needed warmth and building up with good food and a comfortable bed. I sighed and knew we could no longer continue in this 'hand to mouth' existence. As I became more despondent by the minute and lost in my thoughts for our future, I heard a chair noisily scrape behind me.

I turned around to see a middle aged lady stand up and walk towards me. It felt like a dozen heavenly choruses were singing in their loudest voices when the lady stood in front of me and said our names out loud. I nodded, still in state of shock, then she introduced herself as Gerta Coleman and we both fell into her arms, crying tears of joy and relief. I became aware that this feeling was very obviously shared by Gerta who was also crying.

My relief was so strong I felt that I could touch it and embrace it. Finally, we had found the one person who could help us and the relief I felt was enormous, as though a massive boulder had been lifted off my head and I would float away. I could now share the responsibility of Maciej with someone else and this thought made me feel physically lighter.

Once we had all regained our composure, Gerta ushered us to a waiting car and introduced the driver as her neighbour. He told us his name was Mr Logan; he shook hands with both of us and welcomed us to Ireland. I was sure his nose wrinkled a little when we got in the car, this was probably because both of us were in need of a good bath.

We eventually stopped outside two little cottages on the outskirts of Donegal and Gerta indicated for us to go to the one on the right hand side. She then led us into her home. It was a tiny, cosy cottage that reminded me of our flat back home. A small fire burned in the grate and the warmth that emanated from it filled the whole room. We helped Gerta to fill a tin bath with water, which we put in the tiny parlour. It was heavenly scraping the dirt from my skin and feeling clean again.

Our cousin turned out to be a wonderful lady who welcomed us into her life and home with a warm hearted generosity that reminded me of my mother. Maciej were to share the back bedroom. It was bigger than the room we had in Germany and the bed was a great deal more comfortable.

Gerta had already bought new clothes for us as soon as she had heard from the Red Cross. It felt wonderful to be clean, clothed and above all loved. I knew it would take us both a good while to recover from our ordeal but we had made it and were safe which was what my parents wanted.

As time went on, cousin Gerta showered us with love and affection and encouraged us to talk openly about our experiences and suffering. It helped me a great deal to unload the guilt I felt at abandoning my parents. Gerta listened and told me that she would make every effort to locate them. She also explained that if my brother and I had not run we too would have been attacked by the mob, and all my father's planning would have been for nothing. I knew this was true but it did little to ease the ache in my heart.

We had been living in Ireland for around two months when the three of us decided, together, that Maciej and I would change our first names in an effort to integrate ourselves into the country we now called home. We couldn't, however, bring ourselves to abandon our parent's surname. We both knew that we would be eternally grateful for the sacrifice our parents had made for us and hoped that one day, we would meet again. I no longer called myself Levin and answered to Leonard instead, Maciej changed his name to Michael. It was surprising how quickly we became used to our new names.

6

July 4 1937
VIOLET SALTER

The sun burned brightly in a clear blue sky and I loved the feel of the heat caressing my face and warming my bare arms. I was wearing a pale pink sleeveless dress and white sandals; the cotton material of the dress was cooling against my skin. I was making my way to Mrs King's wool shop which I now ran almost single-handedly and I loved every minute of it. The shop and the King family were like a little oasis of love and I felt very content for the first time in my life.

For the last three years I had rented a very pleasant room in a house nearby to where I worked which was fairly cheap. It was very basic with just a narrow single bed shoved up against the end wall. It was iron framed and the thin mattress offered little comfort but that was what I had grown used to, in the children's home, so it didn't bother me. There was a small square table in one corner and a matching chair. I put pennies in the gas metre to keep the place warm and cooked on a small camping stove.

I had made the shabby little room as homely as possible; a few weeks after I moved in I bought a red linen table cloth from a stall at the second hand market. Because the table itself was so small I also managed to make a cushion from the cloth with made the chair a little more comfortable. It was warm and cosy and I enjoyed living on my own after so many years spent sharing a small dormitory with eleven other girls. I loved being self-governing and not reliant on a single person.

The main advantage of where I was living was that low rent amount enabled me to put a fair amount of my wages in the post office each week. I had now amassed a sizeable nest egg which I was saving to buy myself a small house. That was my ultimate dream, to own my own property. I knew this would take many years of working but that didn't faze me. I felt it would give me the ultimate independence I needed and to allow me to stand on my own feet and I couldn't imagine anything better than turning the key in my own door and making my house into a wonderful home.

Life, in general, would have been pretty perfect if it were not for the disturbing rumours circulating about Germany. Apparently, the country's leader, Adolf Hitler, had taken a dislike to any German Jews living in the country and he was literally trying to hound them all out by whatever means he deemed fair.

I hoped that what was being said wasn't true but I doubted it. I felt that the papers would not be able to report that type of news if it was not accurate; I could only hope it was exaggerated and not as bad as what was being written. I couldn't imagine what the Jewish people must feel like when the people they had known all their lives suddenly against them.

I was quite lost in my thoughts as I Rounded the corner to turn into Basset Street, where my place of employment was situated. Due to my attention being elsewhere I almost ran headlong into a man hurrying towards me. I came to an abrupt halt to prevent myself colliding with the person and thought that would teach me to walk along without paying consideration to what was going on around me. Both of us were startled by our near collision and began to apologise in unison.

The last few clouds drifted away and a bright beam of sunlight shone down from the sky as I looked up into the face of the uniformed man I had bumped into. I was instantly transfixed as I gazed into his shining eyes, they were as bright as the sun in the sky above us. I noticed that he had a thin, tanned face that was lit up by the friendliest smile I had ever seen. For a second, it seemed to me that time had stopped as the two of us looked at each other. Finally, the man stuttered:

'Leonard Rosenthal, very pleased to meet you, would you like to come to the pictures with me tonight?'

I surprised myself by immediately agreeing to go on a date with a stranger but it felt right, I wasn't sure why. We arranged for him to meet me outside the shop at closing time that evening; we then both said our goodbyes and continued with our separate journeys. I have no idea why but something inside made it feel as though this was a defining moment in my life. I was absolutely sure that I had just met the man I would marry. Oddly, the thought made me feel warmer still, in the balmy summer day, and I hummed to myself as I unlocked the shop door to begin my days' work.

7

July 4 1937
LEONARD ROSENTHAL

I felt very peculiar, as though I had instantly fallen in love and the feeling scared me a little. Two years previously I had told my auntie Gerta, who was really my second cousin but I called her auntie, that I intended to join the merchant navy. Gerta was extremely proud as was my younger brother Michael. I now spent my time in the navy travelling to various different countries. I soon overcame my initial homesickness and began to enjoy my life at sea.

I wrote to Gerta and Michael every week and they wrote back telling me everything that was going on in their lives. I had had a few girlfriends but, to me, they just seemed like a bit of fun or a distraction from mundane daily chores. I definitely wasn't the stereo typical sailor who had a '*girl in every port*'.

No one I had ever met before had affected me so much and in such a short amount of time as the girl I had almost bumped into. I actually looked up to see if there was a tiny cupid flying above and shooting arrows, randomly, at any passing couple. I had never felt this way about any girl before. I couldn't believe I had just asked her out and I didn't even know her name, but I was glad I had. I knew there was something special about the beautiful girl and I was eager to see her again.

Some hours later as I waited outside the wool shop, a little earlier than arranged, I found myself inexplicably nervous. My collar seemed to be tight enough to strangle me although it had felt fine five minutes previously. When the stunning girl, who I had only met that morning, emerged like a shimmering vision of splendour in the bright sunlight, it almost took my breath away.

She was obviously not surprised to see me and I was glad that she thought me a reliable sort of chap; it was as if she knew in her heart that I would be here. I had grown into a tall slim man and my skin was tanned because of my life on the sea. Instead of the dirty blonde hair I had as a boy it was now golden brown. I hoped my thin nose was softened by my full lips and I smiled the friendliest smile I could as she turned and looked in my direction.

I felt very proud to be wearing my seaman's uniform. It made me feel very dapper and a little handsome. I had shone my shoes so that I could see my face in them and there was not a single crease in my bell-bottom trousers. I offered the young lady my arm in which to link hers and she did so and smiled a smiled that dazzled so much it blocked out the glare of the sun. For a full minute I gazed down at her before pulling myself together and asking what film she would like to watch.

I felt she must be reading my mind when she replied, truthfully, that she did not mind and would prefer to go for a walk as it was a warm day. She went on to say that she had missed the sunshine because she had been stuck indoors for the majority of the day. I told her that that would be great. I was equally happy to be out in the fresh air.

I explained that I had only two days left of shore leave so would much prefer to get to know her before I left. We both walked and talked until late into the night, to the surprise of both of us. She told me her name was Violet and neither she nor I had had any serious partners or been in any long term relationships. Marriage was the last thing on either of our minds. So it was quite a shock to everyone who knew us when we became engaged before I left to join my ship.

8

I treated Lucy Logan, my neighbour's daughter, as if she were my own child. The little girl had been visiting me from the moment she could toddle and I enjoyed her company. I felt that Lucy, and the arrival of Michael and Leonard, had partially filled the void left by the death of my own son, who had been born too early to survive.

Michael and Lucy had become the greatest of friends, almost from the moment he had arrived in Ireland. The boys had arrived four and half years earlier and brought so much joy to my life. There was only about year between Michael and Lucy in age so it was inevitable that they would become playmates and friends. I considered Leonard, Michael and Lucy as close as my own children might have been, had I been lucky enough to have them and was grateful for everyday that they were in my life.

I was pegging my washing on the line one grey but blowy morning when I heard something that surprised me greatly. In the many years that I had lived next door to the Logan's I had never heard a raised voice or a cross word, so I was visibly startled when I heard the sound of crockery being smashed and loud voices screaming at each other.

I quickly finished my chore and to rushed next door, I knew something had obviously upset my dear friends greatly and

I wanted to help them in any way I could; they had been so incredibly kind and supportive to me since Pat, my husband died. I wanted to be there in their time of need also. I knocked on the door and walked in as was normal.

I bustled in as I had done many times before and was about to ask them about their troubles when my question immediately stuck in my throat. I was shocked to the core to be told to go away and never set foot in their house again. I was manhandled out of the door which was then slammed shut by a livid, puce- faced Mr Logan. He pushed out me with such force that I stumbled backwards. I fought to stay upright as I teetered on the two uneven concrete steps.

I would have fallen backwards had it not been for the timely arrival of Michael. He had just finished his morning deliveries for the local shop and was just in time to catch me before I fell. He was puzzled as me when I told him about the goings-on in the Logan household.

After a short discussion we decided to leave the family to their row and maybe call later on in the day when things had calmed a little. I thought I noticed a deep frown from across Michael's brow but it was gone before I knew so I must have imagined it.

A few hours later after I had eaten my tea I decided, somewhat tenuously, to venture next door again to see if I could help. I knocked quietly. I hesitated about walking in unbidden n due to what had happened earlier in the day. I heard no sound from inside the house. After waiting a few minutes, I gently pushed the door open and saw Elsie Logan sitting at her small kitchen table.

Her posture was that of a broken woman and her miserable distress was palpable. She was sitting on one of her rickety kitchen chairs with her arms on crossed on the table and her head lying on them. She was crying bitterly. When I heard the wrenching sobs coming from my dear friend, I rushed forward and bent to hold her and tried to comfort her in some way. I could not imagine what might have happened to cause her so much pain and prayed that there had not been a death in the family.

To my shock and dismay, Elsie Logan, my friend and neighbour for almost twenty years, turned her face towards and hissed at me to get out. I was shocked, confused and stunned and I begged Elsie to tell me what was going on. With undisguised hatred ingrained on every line of her face Elsie told me the Lucy, her beloved only child was pregnant and the baby was Michael's.

Tears rained down Elsie's pale face as she informed me that Lucy's father was, at that very minute, driving her to the priest's house as we spoke. Elsie shouted that the priest would then take Lucy to the laundries, a factory run by nuns, to have her illegitimate bastard and then she could stay and rot there.

Such was my unconcealed shock, I held onto the back of the chair to steady myself stop and me from falling. Such was my utter astonishment I felt as though I had been struck by a physical blow. It took me some minutes to take in what I had been told. In my mind both Lucy and Michael were still children and the idea that they had made a child together didn't seem possible. Michael was barely seventeen years old and Lucy had just turned sixteen but acted much younger due to her parents molly coddling. It felt as though my whole life had been hurled into a whirlpool.

It suddenly dawned on me that Lucy was heading for one of the most hellish places on earth and my shock turned to anger:

'How can you send our beloved Lucy to such a diabolical place, the girl is nothing but a child, why, why?' I implored.

Elsie Logan looked up at me with a look of loathing and disgust:

'She's no daughter of mine, just a filthy whore who lay down with the first man she knew, she's dead to me, I never want her to set foot over my threshold again,' she hissed. I could hardly believe what I was hearing, how could such devoted parents turn on their only child in a heartbeat? I screamed into the twisted, bitter face of the old woman who now seemed like a stranger to me:

'Lucy is just sixteen years old and is an immature child because you and your bloody husband have done nothing but thoroughly spoil her over the years, she's had everything she's ever wanted, how do you imagine she will cope with life at the laundries, both you and I know they are brutal places and the nuns don't have an ounce of compassion in their bodies, surely you don't want Lucy to suffer at their hands?'

Elsie turned and looked at me and her face was now devoid of emotion. She lifted her hand and slapped my cheek with such force it felt as though my teeth rattled. She then screeched at me to leave and told me never to call again.

I stumbled from the property, shaking myself to make sure that I quickly regained control of my battered senses. My face smarted in the cold wind. I raced into my own home and shouted to Michael who came down the stairs two at a time when he heard the despair in my voice. I quickly explained what had happened.

I watched as Michael stood open mouthed before quickly telling me what he had to do. He raced outside and grasped his bicycle that was leant against the cottage wall. He was going to try and stop Mr Logan from taking Lucy to the priest's home.

He knew, without a shadow of a doubt, the bible spouting man would happily deliver her to the doors of hell. It was common knowledge in our small village. The dreaded laundries, as the whole of Ireland knew, were worse than perdition. All the locals were aware that the cruel nuns treated the unfortunate women as little more than slaves and worked them into the ground for many long hours, until virtually the hour before the poor unfortunates gave birth.

Once the child was born it would be adopted with or without the mother's consent. The mother must then remain in the launderette until a respectable man came to free them. Rarely did this happen. Most of those poor women spent their whole lives trapped in these comfortless places; abandoned by their friends and families when their only sin had been to fall in love. This thought drove Michael on even faster. His bicycle wheels left the ground many times as he sped towards the priest's cottage, in the grounds of the village churchyard.

Michael's mind was focussed on saving Lucy as he sped round every corner at breakneck speed. He almost ran into Mr Logan's car, he turned swiftly to the left towards the graveyard and ended up headfirst in the hedge. Mr Logan's vehicle was swiftly jerked to a halt and the angry man leapt out and grabbed Michael roughly by his collar. The young boy was terrified as he could see the complete revulsion and hatred in Lucy's father's eyes.

Michael tried to explain, he knew he was gabbling but he didn't care, he told the incensed man that he would marry

Lucy; there was no need to do any of this and that Lucy didn't belong in the laundry. She was not a fallen woman and he loved her. This seemed to anger Lucy's father even more, he began to shout and rant, his voice screeching to a crescendo, that there was no room for whores in his house. Michael begged him to reconsider but to no avail.

Mr Logan turned towards Michael and raced towards him. Without warning, he began to pummel Michael in the face and body. Michael cried and begged but Mr Logan did not stop until his anger was spent and he had wiped the sweat from his brow. He then got into his car and drove away. Michael told me how he lay on the ground, still and silent as it felt like every part of his body hurt.

Tears fell down his bloodied cheeks as he thought of what Lucy must be going through. He lay back on the moist grass and recalled the one and only time Lucy and he had had sex, so he knew when the baby was due. Angry tears trickled down his cheeks at the sheer helplessness of the situation. There was now absolutely nothing he could do to help Lucy, she was in the hands of the devil and he had put her there.

Michael sobbed like a baby as I held him in my arms and he promised there and then that he would go and free Lucy as soon as the child was born, he would make sure she knew that he would never abandon her. It took an immense effort for Michael to drag his battered body from the ground and pick up his discarded bike. He leant heavily on it as he made the agonising journey back home to me, one of the few people in this world who loved him and would try and help him through the tough days ahead.

I tended to Michael's wounds, as he told me exactly what

had happened between him and our neighbour, but I could not soothe his tormented mind. I worried that he had suffered far too much in his short life and wished there was something I could do to prevent his further heartache but the state of affairs was out of both our hands and all we could do was wait until the baby was born. My dear Michael was still a child and he had lost everything. First he had lost his parents and his home and now Lucy and his child.

It would be difficult for the hardiest of people to bear and Michael was a sensitive soul. I worried about him constantly but could not help him. Each day after work Michael would cycle furiously towards the home for unmarried mothers, where he knew Lucy was imprisoned. I begged him to come home instead, I told him there was nothing to gain by standing outside the place, but I couldn't stop him. He would sit outside for up to four hours at a time to try and catch a glimpse of Lucy.

He explained that he hoped she would know he was there and that she was not alone. If she looked out of one of the small windows and saw him, she would know that he was waiting for her. The building was enormous. It had thick grey walls with tiny windows that couldn't possibly have let much light into the place. The building was dark and spooky and had the appearance of death, at least in my mind, and I was quite sure none of the poor inmates saw the brightness of day.

Sometimes, he told me, he thought he could hear the screams of the pregnant women giving birth. He said it felt as though his heart was being twisted violently when he thought of Lucy alone, in the cold, loveless place. Sometimes he viewed the luscious grassy hills surrounding the forbidding building and he felt as though he would go totally insane. I tried to talk him out of tormenting himself on a daily basis but I was quite sure my words fell on deaf ears because he continued his vigil of the forbidding building.

He told me how he often contemplated breaking in and dragging her out but could not work out how to get into the building. The home was completely surrounded by a high concrete wall with weeds and foliage jutting out of several ragged crevices and a pair of enormous iron gates.

Embedded in the top of the wall, dotted along at close intervals, were jagged pieces of glass that glinted in the sunlight and reminded everyone of the plight of the inmates. Michael knew the place was virtually impenetrable and this frustrated him further and his helplessness made him angry.

Michael told me he was unsure if the glass and gates were there to keep the inmates in or the visitors out. His sweet little face was red with embarrassment as he explained to me what had happened between him and Lucy. He grimaced as he recalled their immature fumbling's that had lasted just seconds but had ruined so many lives forever. My heart broke for the vulnerable child and I yearned to turn the clock back and save him from all he had suffered.

Many months later, when Michael arrived back at the shop, where he worked, on a grey October day, his employer informed him that I had been in and asked him to go straight home instead of going to the laundries. Michael asked why but I had given the man no other information. When he arrived home, I watched through the kitchen window as Michael hurled his bike into the hedge and bounded in. I was about to impart more devastating news and I wished with all my heart that I had something joyful to tell him.

Immediately he could see that I had been crying, because of my red, puffy face, and he ran over to comfort me. I patted his hand lovingly and gestured for him to sit down. He perched obediently on the edge of the chair. He was clearly, overly eager to know what I had to tell him and his body shook. I took a deep breath because I knew that what I was going to tell him would break his heart in two, as it had mine.

In as gentle and calming voice I could, I took a deep breath and explained that Lucy had given birth to a baby boy but he had not survived. I swallowed deeply as I explained that Lucy was also in hospital and was also not expected to live. I couldn't soften the blow and the look on Michaels face would haunt me for the rest of my days. It looked like someone had struck Michael with a thunderbolt. It was evident that he could scarcely believe what was happening by the dumfounded expression on his face.

He looked at me helplessly, shaking in head and pushing his fingers through his thick unruly hair. I would have given anything to take his pain away; I knew the deep hurt it felt to lose a beloved child. Without warning, he raced out of the kitchen and outside. I watched as he mounted his bicycle and pedalled feverishly away.

Michael explained later that his only thought had been to see Lucy. He had arrived in a very small amount of time bathed in sweat and dishevelled from his journey. On arrival at the hospital he ran towards the double doors of the ancient medical building.

As he neared them, they were pushed slowly open and Mr and Mrs Logan walked out through them. They looked as though they had aged twenty years in the last six months. He watched as Lucy's parents emerged into the cold, grey day. All three pairs of eyed stared intently at each other until Mr Logan spat:

'You've done now boy, you gone and killed her.' They shoved past Michael without a backward glance.

Refusing to believe what he had heard Michael ran away the couple and raced towards the reception. He was directed to a sideward where a nurse was awaiting his arrival. The kindly lady grasped both his hands as she explained that Lucy was gravely ill and was losing her battle for life but that they would continue to fight for her. She then gently led him to a curtained off bed in the corner of the white, clinical room. A chair was placed by the side of the bed and he silently sat.

Michael looked at the face of his beloved Lucy and was certain that death was close by. He wanted to swot it away like an annoying fly but knew that was not possible. He reached out and held Lucy's soft, cold hand. Her beautiful face was a deathly shade of grey and her breathing was laboured. He stood and gently kissed on her cheek then he began to talk as he squeezed her hand tighter still in an effort to let her know he was close by:

'Hello Lucy, sorry for everything that has happened to you but from now on things are going to get better, don't go sweetheart, please stay, we're going to get married and have a wonderful life together, we'll have a tiny cottage with roses around the door and we'll have more children and nobody will take them away from us, I promise' He allowed his tears to fall unashamedly down his cheeks as he continued:

'You are going to wear the most beautiful dress made of golden taffeta and hold a bouquet of the reddest roses I can find, with little shamrocks pushed in between, we'll decorate the church in Donegal with as many wild flowers as we can find and we'll invite the whole village to watch us become man and wife.' He gazed at Lucy, longing to see some sign of life on her alabaster face:

'Of course Len will be my best man and Violet will be your maid of honour, we're going to have the best life together, my love,' Michael stroked Lucy's soft cheek as he said this then kissed her gently on the lips.

'We'll have a lovely long, life together, us and our children; I promise Lucy my love, so please stay.'

For three days and nights he barely slept, he just talked to Lucy, willing her to live with every syllable, wanting to breathe his life into hers with his own breath. The nurses supplied him with endless cups of tea and kindness I brought him food and sat with Lucy, at times, so he could catch a bit of sleep. On the third day Michael and I were both sure that Lucy's pallor was less grey and more the colour of white porcelain, I hoped it wasn't wishful thinking.

The medical staffs were sceptical but we never gave up hope. Silently I urged Lucy to fight and to stay alive because she had so much to live for. Watching Michael go through this torment was tearing me apart; I felt helpless and useless but stayed with him all the same. The, one magical, glorious day our prayers were answered. We both stood back, as we had done many times before, and watched as a nurse gave Lucy some more medication through the drip in her arm and then we heard her. Her voice was as soft as the breeze and barely audible and we strained to hear as she muttered:

'I hurt.'

Michael rushed forward and cupped her cold face in his warm hands and smiled down at her. I draw a cross on my chest with my finger and thanked the Almighty God for giving Lucy another chance, I knew that, in His eyes, she was a sinner but I prayed for forgiveness for her. The nurse spoke briefly to Lucy then rushed off in search of a doctor as Michael and Lucy looked into one another's eyes:

'The baby?' I heard Lucy whisper, struggling to get the words out:

'A boy,' Michael answered quietly then he gulped deeply.

A tear fell down his cheek as he explained that the child was born dead, unable to take a breath in this world. Salty tears rained down Lucy's hollow cheeks as she fell back into a deep sleep. Michael tenderly wiped them off her face with his sleeve then sat and laid his head in his arms and slept, still holding Lucy's hand.

I made certain that the hospital workers had been made aware of Lucy's inhuman treatment by the cold, uncaring nuns at the laundries. They, in turn, explained to Michael and me that they had left Lucy in labour for too long and her baby had become trapped in the birth canal and suffocated. The heavy handed methods that the wretched women had used to try and birth the baby had damaged Lucy internally and it would be some time before she was fit to leave the confines of the hospital.

The general concern was that Lucy's parents would come back to claim her and, worse still, might send he back to the nuns, as was their prerogative as parents of a child. No one wanted that to happen therefore a cloak of secrecy was thrown around the whole situation with everyone involved sworn to secrecy about the survival of Lucy Logan. The gossip in the village was that Lucy Logan had passed away and her parents had allowed her a pauper's funeral which no one had attended.

A month later, in a clandestine operation, Lucy was released from the hospital; the local doctor picked both her and Michael up in his ancient motor car accompanied by me. As we were driven to the ferry port I explained what was happening. It had been arranged that Michael and Lucy would go to Bristol to live with Len and his wife, Violet. They were expecting them. Lucy did not acknowledge any of this, she just sat still and staring in the back of the vehicle, swaddled in blankets and held tightly by Michael.

Michael wrote and told me, on his arrival in England, that it was not until he and Lucy were aboard the boat that the pounding in his chest lessened. Every movement was painfully slow because Lucy was still very weak and had to be helped aboard by himself and the doctor. I had provided them with food and money. Michael was so grateful to me for recuing him for a second time that when we embraced at the quayside, tears stung the corners of his eyes and he said it felt as though he would choke.

I held him tightly and told him to take care of Lucy and he promised he would. They were both immensely relieved when they finally arrived on English soil. A train journey took them to Bristol where Violet and Len stood on the platform awaiting their arrival. Len was muscular and well-built, due to his work on board ship, and he immediately scooped Lucy up in his arms and carried her to the waiting taxi. He was due back in service the following day but sat that evening talking to Michael.

He explained to his younger brother that Lucy would need a lot of care and that it was a big responsibility resting on Michael's young shoulders. The brothers chatted on and Michael promised he would do all he could to aid Lucy's recovery. He explained that he was afraid and felt out of his depths but that all also blamed himself for all the suffering that Lucy had had to endure and would do everything in his power to make her well again.

The following months were very difficult for the family. Lucy was very weak and unwell but this could be cured with rest and medication. It was her sadness of mind that was the hardest thing to change. Tears constantly dripped down her sorrow-filled blue eyes and the colour refused to return to her face. Violet sat with her as much as she could and spent hours listening to the young girl when she told her of the guilt that ate away at her soul.

Lucy explained that she was sure that her son had died because she was being punished by God. Violet explained that God was not vengeful and he would never cause harm to an innocent. She went on to say that the only people who were responsible were the loveless nuns and their sanctimonious preaching; professing to be children of God but treating desperate young girls like bits of dirt. Violet was sure that the evil women didn't have a religious bone in their entire bodies and all they had were wickedness in their uncaring hearts.

After many months the colour began to return to Lucy's cheeks and her strength returned. Both Violet and Lucy knew she would never fully get over the loss of her son and the harsh treatment by her parents and the nuns; but all who knew her were sure that she would recover. Lucy slowly began to regain the will and power to face the future and plan what lay ahead. Michael became entwined in their shared loss of their son and they became to soul mates that clung onto each other like survivors of a shipwreck clinging to a rock.

9

September 3 1939
VIOLET SALTER

It was humid day in early September as I walked, with some effort, along the cobbled street to Kings Wool and Sewing Accessories, the shop where I had once worked. Cotton wool clouds floated in the clear blue sky as the rays of the golden sun caressed my face and neck and enveloped my body in a blanket of uncomfortable heat. By the time I arrived at the shop and it felt like I sweating from every pore in my body, even though I was only wearing a thin cotton dress and sandals, the heat was so intense it seemed to have sapped all my energy away.

The shop bell clanged noisily and I entered. Mary Dunstan was standing behind the counter engrossed in the order book. She was my former employer's daughter who was now doing the job that I once did. She looked up, startled by the noise of the shop bell and the door scraping against the hard, shiny floor. I smiled and was happy to see that she couldn't disguise her joy at seeing me and the feeling was mutual.

Over the years we had become very good friends, due to our shared interest in the shop and the love for her elderly parents. She watched as I dabbed my sweaty face with my handkerchief then rushed forward quickly, and helped me walk towards a small chair to the side of the counter. I sat heavily and gratefully. I was glad to take the weight off my swollen feet and ankles.

I was enormous and feeling like a baby elephant. Being almost nine months pregnant with my first child, I had come to realise that carrying a baby in the middle of a shimmering hot summer's day was no easy task. The heat was beginning to make me feel distinctly unwell and, due to my advanced state of confinement and the sweltering temperature, I couldn't wait for the baby to be born.

I sat and waited as Mary served an elderly lady who had come into buy some knitting needles. Mary showed the lady several pairs and the customer finally chose what she wanted and walked from the premises with a beaming smile that showed she was happy with her purchase. I fanned my face and body with a knitting pattern from the box on the counter. Once I had rested a moment or two, and the shop was empty, Mary indicated that we should go into the back room.

This meant that I could see my former employers, whom I loved as though they were my own family. On some of my previous visits the elderly couple had not been well enough for a visit but today they were both obviously well enough to see me. I waddled after her as soon as we entered the coolness of the room had an immediate effect on me and I instantly felt more comfortable. Both the windows to the back of the property and a delightful cooling breeze wafted around the room.

Mr King, Mary's elderly father, lay in a single bed with an iron bedstead against the wall at the far side of the room. He was propped up on several pillows and cushions. Although he seemed to be comfortable his skin was paper thin and it looked transparent. There was not an ounce of fat on his skinny body.

I loved the kindly old man and wished there was more I could do to ease his suffering. Today, unusually, he was not swathed in several blankets and I felt the warmth on his soft cheek as I kissed him.

I lumbered over to the nearest chair and was happy to see that the warm weather had put some colour into his normally pallid face. He smiled a watery smile at me then patted my clammy hand. I then turned my attention to Mrs King, his wife who had taught me everything I know about running a wool shop. She had been sitting in an upright armchair next to the bed knitting, on my arrival, but now she stood with arms aloft and walked towards me. The elderly woman then bent down embraced me warmly.

She remarked on my advanced pregnancy and I nodded and smiled, thankful to take the weight off my feet. Mary Dunstan left the room and re-entered with a tray of glasses and a bottle of homemade lemonade which she passed to the occupants of the room. I drank my thirstily and it tasted like nectar as it slid down my dry throat. We all drank eagerly as the weather had caused all to become dehydrated. I watched as Mary gently helped her father sip at his until he could manage no more then she gently wiped his lips.

Mary Dunstan, her mother and I were in the small kitchen behind the shop. There was a table in the centre with a blue Formica top and four chairs pushed under each side. Against the wall was a fireplace with an unlit fire. It was however, prepared to be ignited, should the weather turn cold. It had a layer of newspaper, scrunched into balls at the base which was covered by several sticks of wood, layered in a criss-cross pattern with a shovel full of coal covering it. There were two straight backed arm chairs either side of the hearth which were now occupied by me and Mrs King. Mr King's bed was wedged against the wall beside my chair and this enabled me to hold his hand as I sat.

Mary took the tray of empty glasses into the scullery to the back of the room then pulled out a kitchen chair and sat down. We all chatted amicably to one another about not much at all. Mrs King discussed the weather and everyday mundane occurrences. We were all just contended to be in each other's company. Mr King listened in with interest into the conversation around him and nodded in agreement every now and then.

Leonard and I had been married for nine months and the speediness of our meeting and marriage still astounded me and everyone else present. It soon became the next topic and we all shook our heads, as we had done many times before, exclaiming at how lucky Leonard and I were to have met each other and fallen in love. Leonard was away at sea and was due home in a few weeks, hopefully in time for the birth of our first child. The hours sped by and I was surprised to realise that the afternoon was rapidly tuning into evening.

As the day began to draw to a close and I readily accepted the invitation to join the family for tea, I often felt lonely when Leonard was at sea and loved being in the company of others. Mary's husband, Timothy, duly arrived home from work and soon we were all tucking into an egg salad with new potatoes crusty homemade bread. My lifelong dream had finally come true when Leonard and I had bought lovely cottage in a terraced street. It was not far from the wool shop where I once worked. It was our own little love nest I adored making the place homely and comfortable.

Once the food was finished, we all gathered around the newly acquired wireless. All of us enjoyed the songs played on the radio and we first listened to Glenn Miller singing Moonlight Serenade. His voice was so velvety it reminded of melted chocolate and I became lost in the soothing melody. Next came the dulcet tones of the Andrews sisters which made my foot tap involuntarily and I wished Len was here to share this wonderful evening.

After around ten minutes of music the radio became silent then crackled loudly before a familiar voice sounded through the speakers. The music had been interrupted by a news bulletin read out by the prime minister, Neville Chamberlain. I was puzzled and a little worried but was unsure why. I sat quietly and listened, as did the rest of the inhabitants of the room.

I felt Mr King squeeze my hand a little tighter and I put my other one over the top of his to offer him a little comfort but I was unsure of why he might need it. The stoic voice announced that Germany had invaded Poland against the will of Great Britain and that they had no choice but to declare war. For a few seconds the room was deadly silent.

I was profoundly shocked and it seemed that so were the rest of the occupants in the room judging by the expression on their faces. The last thing I had heard from our prime minister during a broadcast some days previously was that there would be 'peace in our time' and I was enormously relieved. Now, we were being told that Britain was at war with Germany and the enormity of what the cold voice had said had stunned all in the room. I was terrified, I don't know if it was the fear of the unknown or the worry of being blown to bits by a German bomb but I began to tremble.

Mr King pulled his covers up from the base of his bed and closer around his body, as though the announcement of war had made him feel cold once more. A single tear rolled down his soft veiny, cheek. Mrs King sat with her head in her hands while Mary and Timothy sat gazing at each other with an expression of horror on their startled faces. I also thought that the war that had been fought just twenty years previously was supposed to be the war that ended all wars. I felt as though the world was going mad. Why would anyone bring death and destruction to innocent people?

My thoughts drifted to Len. I wondered if he would be safe and prayed to God that he would. I needed him now, much more than I ever had done before. The onset of war had made me feel vulnerable and small. I felt like the small child I once was, locked in the darkness of the cellar, feeling like I was the only person left in the world. The isolation was the only thing that bothered me about the punishment at the children's home. Now I felt strangely secluded once more even though I was sitting in a crowded room surrounded by people I loved.

I yearned for the comfort and protection of Len's masculine arms around my shoulders and wanted to hear him promise me that everything would be alright. That did not happen as Leonard was in the middle of the ocean and I wondered if he had heard the devastating news. Eventually, Timothy spoke in a monotone voice declaring that there was nothing we could do accept get on with things. Still, we all sat, like statues in a museum unsure what to do or what to say.

At that precise moment a sound, like a screeching cat, reverberated around the whole room, shaking us all out of our astonished daze. I stood and looked questioningly at everyone, sweat gathered on my brow as I wondered if this was to be the moment my life ended. I listened for the sound of a bomb dropping or the sound of a German soldier marching in and shooting us all. Timothy ordered us all to stay put then he raced outside into the street. He returned a few minutes and announced, with obvious relief, that it was just a practise run for when the real warning was needed.

This was to be the warning for any air raids we might suffer in the future. He explained that when he sounded we all had to find a place of safety because it indicated that the enemy was on its way to drop bombs on us and our homes. I felt hot, sick and dizzy all at once. As I began to sway I groped the seat I had just risen from and slid back into it. There were no words to describe what I felt or stifle the fear that silently invaded my mind and oozed from every pore in my body. It was as though I had been electrocuted by a dagger of lightning and the sensation had paralysed me.

In my confused and shocked mind, I saw my whole future disappear in a cloud of smoke. What would happen to Leonard and my unborn child, were our lives going to be snuffed out as though we were as inconsequential as a common house fly? Some part of my ruptured thinking began to register an uncommon sensation. I felt a warm dampness between my legs and was momentarily dismayed and a little embarrassed. Mary rushed to my aid. She held my hand and gently told me that my waters had broken. She explained that my labour had started.

I looked at her questioningly as she heaved me to my feet, still in a dazed state of shock after hearing the dreadful news. Between the two of us, we managed to stagger out of the small room then struggle up the narrow stairway together. We entered the tiny box sized bedroom. I leaned against the wall to steady myself then Mary led me to a stool in the corner of the room and gently pressed me down onto it. She then proceeded to cover the bed in old newspapers, provided by Mrs King. I started to babble that my baby wasn't due yet.

Mary held both my shoulders firmly and informed me that the baby had other ideas. The firm tone in her voice made me aware that I had actually absorbed what she was saying. Without warning, a spasm of pain gripped me, like a metal belt tightening around my middle. The ferocity of the agony took my breath away and I screamed loudly.

Mary instructed me to try and stay calm and told me that she had sent to get the local mid-wife. As another contraction wracked my entire body, I sank to my knees beside the bed and bit into the lilac candlewick bedspread to try and manage the excruciating pain that was pulsating through my body.

With the next excruciating contraction, I felt an overwhelming urge to push and there was nothing in the world anyone could do to stop me. My whole body convulsed and writhed and as the agony threatened to overwhelm me. I felt that I had lost all control of my life and my body. As I screamed that I could no longer take any more pain, I felt a heavy warmth slide from my body and the hurting stopped. It was as abrupt as fork of lightning illuminating the sky then disappearing just as quickly in to the dark night.

Mary rushed forward and caught the tiny baby as my knees gave way and I fell to the floor in a state of total bewilderment. I was breathless as both of us gazed, in wonderment, at the perfectly formed little human being with tears falling down our cheeks. I could hardly believe that I was now a mother. It was a joyous and overwhelming feeling and I could not stop staring at the new life I had created.

The first thing the mid-wife saw when she bustled into the room was Mary and I gazing at the new born. It felt to me as though time had stood still. Thankfully, the very capable lady quickly took charge of the situation. She cut the infants cord and wrapped her in a soft blanket, she then handed the baby to Mary. Once this was done the nurse helped me onto the bed and saw to my needs.

The sympathetic mid wife took my temperature and my blood pressure. She then weighed and checked my new daughter and declared us both fit and well. I actually felt as though an imaginary steam train had hit me but I knew that I was just feeling a little shocked after the speedy delivery. Mary handed me my child then left the room to make us all a much needed cup of tea. I let myself sink back into the softness of the pillows; I still felt utter disbelief as into stared into the tiny face of my new born daughter.

I realised that in less than an hour I had given birth to a daughter. A small pang of regret hit me when I realised that I had brought a child into a world at war. As the tears threatened I quickly pulled myself together. I became aware that I was responsible for someone who could not look after herself and was totally reliant on me, now was not the time for regrets or self-pity. That time had passed and now I had to do the very best I could for my little girl.

As it was, there was little I could do about anything that was going on in the wider world so I set about the practicalities of feeding my baby. As she tugged at my breast I felt a sense of fulfilment and well-being envelop my whole body, it was as though this was what I had been born for. I suddenly felt, in sharp contrast to my initial feeling, swiftly and totally at peace with the world, cocooned in my tiny realm of joy and contentment. I had a daughter and all I wanted to do was love and protect her for the rest of my life.

I stayed with the Kings for a week before I was fully recovered and able to leave and take care of my baby. I apologised to my lovely friends for all the trouble I had caused but they assured that me I was very welcome and had been no trouble at all. Mr King had cried tears of sheer elation when I placed my tiny bundle of happiness in his reedy arms. It was one of those beautiful moments that I would remember always. To me, it was symbolic of the very old and the new born reaching across the years and diminishing them.

Tim had brought the ancient pram over from the small cottage the Len and I now owned and parked it in the yard at the back of the shop. I placed my tiny child into the carriage nestled her into blankets, even though it was still a very warm September day; I needed to make sure she was warm. The sky was a beautiful clear blue and the birds soared lazily above, immune to the disquiet of the country.

There was no indication that Britain was at war and this gave me a semblance of comfort and calm. I could still scarcely believe that I was the mother of this beautiful baby and wandered how my mother had felt when she discovered that she was pregnant.

I felt myself pitying the poor woman who was unmarried and about to be saddled with an illegitimate baby but wished that she had lived so that we could have met and discussed the joys of mother hood. I had written to tell Len about his new daughter but knew that, sometimes, the letters I sent could take weeks to reach the sailors. I was excitedly looking forward to his leave in a few weeks' time when he would get to meet his firstborn; I swear I could see a lot of Len's features in his daughter but maybe not, maybe I just wanted to see it.

A few weeks later, I was pushing the pram along the narrow pavement desperately trying to avoid all the cracks and tree roots that threatened to tip the perambulator over. Such was my concentration on my task that it took several minutes for me to register what the local newspaper seller was repeating over and over again. My little bubble of happiness punctured and disappeared as what he was saying filtered through, into the fuzzy channels of my mind.

When it finally did, I froze, feeling almost paralysed by horror as I heard the man shouting the headlines over and over again. He kept shouting the same headline at anyone close enough to hear. A ship called The Teakwood had been torpedoed as it delivered supplies to those that needed it. All lives aboard were lost and presumed dead. The words were whirling around in my mind like the colours in a kaleidoscope. I had to physically shake my head to clear it.

I knew, for sure, that Len was on board the Teakwood. My strength suddenly seemed to leave my body as though it had been sucked out by an invisible force. I staggered towards a nearby bench, leaning heavily on the handle of the pram. I needed to sit and catch my breath. I held tightly onto the bench as I kicked the brake of the stroller on as though on auto pilot. A middle aged lady leant over and asked me if I was alright. I nodded and she walked away.

I wish I hadn't pretended that I was fine because a kind of weakness overwhelmed me and made my body sag onto the seat. It took a tremendous amount of effort to swallow the ball tears that seemed to be lodged in my throat and not to allow them to spill from eyes and scream like a wounded animal. I could hardly believe what I had heard; could I be a widow already? I needed to pull myself together, I felt as though I was in danger of fainting and I had my daughter to think about.

I took some deep and calming breaths in an effort to slow the fast beating of my heart. This seemed to help and I jumped up and began to push the pram, hurriedly, towards the Kings Wool shop. I hardly remembered the short journey and paid no attention to the uneven pavement as I made my desperate journey to the only people who I thought could help me. I arrived at my destination and hastily parked the pram outside, after wrenching the brake into place I burst through the shop door.

Both old Mrs King and her daughter, Mary Dunstan, were behind the counter and both were serving customers. I stood and waited. My agitation was threatening to spill over and seemed like an age for the customers to be served. I could see Mrs King looking at me with obvious concern as I waited. Finally the customers had been dealt with and as soon as they were out the door I lunged forward and gabbled, almost incoherently, the terrible news I had just heard from the newspaper seller.

Mary rushed forward and tried to usher me into the back of little shop but I stopped her and explained about the baby outside. She nodded then went out the front door I watched as she jerked the pram free then pushed it around the side to the shop. I guessed she was taking it to the alley that led to the back gate of the shop and into the small yard. Here was the outdoor toilet and a small sheltered area. When Mary joined Mrs King and me in the back room, she explained that she had left my baby in the shade of the high concrete wall.

I thanked her but was not really thinking about my daughter. I knew Mary would make sure she was safe and comfortable. Mrs King brought a tray of tea in, from the scullery, and spooned a large helping of sugar into mine. Strangely the sickly sweetness of the drink seemed to soothe my shredded nerves a little bit.

When Mary relayed the news to Old Mr King he was visibly shocked and saddened and I rushed to comfort him. He quickly regained his composure and screwed up his face as began trying to think of a way that he could get some information about Len. He was a little at a loss and told us all so as we all stood and looked at him, waiting for any instruction that might help. All he could think of was the war office but didn't think they would know much yet as none of us knew hoe recently the incident had occurred.

To all our relief, Tim, Mary's husband, arrived at the house a few minutes after I had. As soon as he had the news he turned, he placed his hat back on his head and left again to try and find out some information about what had happened to the Teakwood. I waited anxiously, so very glad to be with my friends at this terrible time when I felt I was in some kind of limbo land. Tim arrived back to the shop a small time later with very little in the way of news. He had gone to the police station because he could think of nowhere else to go.

The sergeant had contacted a friend from the newspaper office but they could only tell him that the ship had been hit by a torpedo and it was not known if there were any survivors. I felt deflated, as though someone had punched the life from me and was totally unsure of what to do or where to go from here.

Was I supposed to just wait and see if my husband was alive or dead? It seemed cruel and inhuman but there was obviously nothing that anyone could do. Mary and Mrs King both insisted that I stay with them, I thanked them but I refused. I explained that if Len had died, I would have to get used to being on my own so I may as well start now.

I went onto explain I was going to wait until Len came home so we could think of a name for our daughter together but I now decided I better get on with it, in case he did not return at all. Even thinking that he might be dead made me feel angry and as though I was letting Len down somehow but I had to be practical.

We all sat for a moment, deep in thought and then Mary asked me if I had any ideas about a name for my daughter. I would have liked to have named her after my childhood friend Jean but that would only remind me of the orphanage and I preferred to forget that episode of my life.

I asked Mrs King what her name was and when the old lady told me it was Hester, my mind was made up. My daughter would be named Hester Jean Rosenthal. Mrs King had tears in her pale blue eyes when she heard my decision and hugged me tightly. She told me not to give up hope until I had solid news of lens fete and I promised her I wouldn't.

As I prepared to leave and I thanked the family profusely for all their support and promised I would let them know the minute I heard any news, whether it was good or bad. I then collected the pram from the back yard. As I manoeuvred it out of the back gate my daughter stirred. Her tiny lashes fluttered open and vibrant blue yes stared at me that were a mirror image of Lens. I hoped, with all my heart, he would get to meet his beautiful child.

As I walked back to the little cottage I shared with Len I didn't know if I should be upset or hopeful. I felt that I would know, in my heart, if my husband was dead but then dismissed that as a fanciful notion that only had a place in romantic stories. Later that evening as I sat feeding baby Hester I became lost in my thoughts. I hoped that if Len was dead that it had been quick and he had not had a chance to feel fear or pain. It had been two weeks since the announcement about the war, on the radio, but nothing had remotely changed and life seemed to carry on as it always had done.

If I had not heard about the attack on the Teakwood I would have decided, like a lot of other people I knew did, that it was a phoney war but this event had brought it straight to the core of my life. I stood and looked out of my small kitchen window. An Anderson shelter had been erected at the end of the street and the local football pitch was being dug up to plant vegetables. Strange inflatables, known as barrage balloons, were seen bobbing high in the sky above me. I wandered, had the government secretly expected the war but kept us all in the dark; they seemed to be very well prepared for it.

Once I had settled Hester into her cot, I set about the task of clearing the rubbish from the cupboard under the stairs. It was a large space that might give us shelter from any falling bombs and I now knew I should prepare for the worst. The war was definitely no longer phoney for me and the time had come for practicalities, not hoping and wishing that we were still living in peace. The war had banged on my door and almost kicked it in. I felt I owed to Len to protect our daughter when he was unable to.

10

September 13 1939
Leonard Rosenthal

I was lying on my bunk in my billet aboard the tanker, Teakwood, eagerly telling anyone who would listen about my keenly awaited child and my gorgeous wife, Violet. I explained that I was hoping for a son but didn't really mind as long as Violet and the baby were alright. I had been in the merchant navy since I was sixteen years old and loved my job very much but I don't mind admitting, that I was as shocked at the rest of the crew when we were told that Britain was at war.

We were all informed by our superior officers that it was now our duty to keep the country fed as best we could in the coming months or years. I hoped that Violet was alright and not feeling too frightened. It must have been a shock, for her, when she heard that England was at war with Germany. I was very glad she had Mary Dunstan and Mr and Mrs King as friends, they were good people and I knew would take care of her. Tim Dunstan, Mary's husband, had told me as much, a few months back, when we had met and had a beer at our local pub.

The baby was due around now but I had been reliably informed that first babies seldom arrived on time and that I would, undoubtedly, be on shore leave around the time of the birth. Secretly, I hoped Violent would give birth before I docked. I had no wish to be anywhere close to a woman giving birth. I had heard various horror stories from my shipmates about blood curdling screams and mess. I was happy to leave the birthing of children to the women as it was supposed to be.

As the craft sailed towards England; there was an air of joviality aboard as everyone was happily excited that we would be home with our loved ones within the next few weeks. Although I loved sailing I also missed Violet very much and was eagerly waiting to hold her in my arms once more. I constantly looked at my precious black and white photograph of her smiling widely outside the King's shop. It always warmed my heart, even on the coldest day.

It had been a long and trying shift, one where everything seemed to go wrong and I was all of a fluster. There was no reason for this; it was just one of those things that life threw at one occasionally. As I worked, buried deep inside the hold of the ship, I tried to compose myself and calm down. I spun round when I heard the unmistakeable sound of the ships hooter; it was unusual to hear it as it was a warning of danger.

We were far too close to England to be near any icebergs so I couldn't work out what the threat could be. I was instantly puzzled as to why it would be sounding at our present destination, where there were no shipping hazards or other vessels crossing our paths.

I gasped audibly and grasped a hand rail as I felt the ship shudder violently to one side then it began to list precariously, making it difficult for me to stay on my feet. I felt very vulnerable, down in the bowels of the vessel working alone.

A second warning hooter rang out. From previous training sessions, I knew this meant that we were facing imminent danger and that we should all head for our action stations. I raced up the steel stairway, two steps at a time. My heart was thudding and my mouth was dry, I had no idea what was happening. I needed to know what had caused the sturdy ship to lean so dangerously. I looked about at the rest of the crew.

It would seem to anyone watching from afar that the whole ship was in a scene of chaos and shouting but, in actual fact, each man knew where he should be and was running furiously towards their position. I had served with the merchant navy for four years and I had never experienced anything like what was happening now. There had been a few rough crossings when we'd sailed in heavy, stormy seas but that was to be expected. Fear seeped into my bones, I felt almost as frightened as I did when my brother and I fled across Germany.

I was acutely aware that my former homeland was now the enemy and I was sickened but not shocked. I vividly remembered my former neighbours being beaten and, in my mind, I relived the sight of my mother and father being attacked in the street. Once I reached the deck I quickly looked around to try and establish exactly what was happening.

I rapidly realised things were not as they should be. Men were peering over the side as the ship listed more and more. After another violent lurch from the floundering vessel I grasped onto the ship railings and clung on for dear life to stop myself sliding across the deck.

My commanding officer shouted an order and I stood to attention, as best I could on the listing vessel. My CO informed us that we had been hit by an enemy torpedo and that the boat was sinking fast, he ordered everyone to the life rafts. I was pushed along in the throng of bodies heading towards the east of the ship. I was now absolutely terrified. I tried to swallow my fear but it continuously rose up in my throat making me feel sick.

The reason for my terror was that, despite the number of years I had served in the navy, I was still unable to swim. I looked down into the swirling ocean. The dark green, almost blackness of the water made me think that I would be swallowed up by its vastness. I gulped deeply to try and push down the dread rising up in my stomach but I was not successful. Only the mass of bodies squashed on the deck kept me upright and I became convinced that my time was up and that I was about to die. I prayed to God to take care of Violet and the baby if my premonition came true.

I suddenly became aware that, above all the noise of the listing ship and heaving sea I could clearly head the concise voice of my sergeant Major. He was now yelling, ordering all of us to stay put. No one questioned the superior office but we all wondered what his plan was. As I stood to attention, as best I could, it seemed to me the boat was leaning a little less or was it my hopeful imagination? As I waited, I thought about my life in Germany and how it had turned bad so quickly. The sadness at my family's plight never left me.

In my nightmares, I saw my mother and father being beaten and abused and often wandered if I would ever see them again. I very much doubted it. Once Michael and I had both settled in Ireland with aunty Gerta, we had tried all means we could to discover the fate of our parents.

The Red Cross and the Salvation Army had exhausted all avenues in their search for Phineas and Hana Rosenthal. News filtering out about the treatment of Jews in Germany was terrifying and we knew, first hand, that it was all true and not the propaganda that the German Chancellor professed it to be.

Apparently Adolf Hitler had ordered that all Jewish people, who were living and working in Germany, could not be permitted to run a business and were being stripped of any assets they owned. There were rumours about them being herded into giant ghettos and being forced to wear yellow stars on their sleeves. This was to make the German population aware of their Jewish origins. I was loath to believe that this could be true and felt distraught for my fellow Jews and fervently hoped that things were not as bad as they seemed.

An icy wind blew unexpectedly across the crowded deck and I felt a shiver run through my body. I hoped that none of the stories about the German Jews were true but in my heart I knew they probably were. The ripples of war had begun many years earlier and Michael and I were lucky to have escaped, I only wished my parents had been able to also.

As I desperately tried to shake the memories from my head I came to realise that the boat, although not stable, was not definitely listing as badly as it had been. The commander was informing us that the evacuation was no longer necessary and we should all make our way back to our stations. I'm sure the relief I felt was palpable as I gulped deep breaths of salty air.

After a tense half hour or so as we all waited patiently, we were informed that we were going to continue with our journey back to Dover and, with Gods help, the vessel might make it. I was not the only man to get down on my knees and thank the Lord above for saving us. I was in no doubt at all that the Great Man had come to our rescue and I vowed to spend more time worshipping auntie Gerta's chosen God once my feet touched dry land.

The damage to the vessel meant the trip would take twice as long but it didn't matter. I and everyone else were mightily thankful not to be floating in the Atlantic in a small life boats with no food, water or direction. As I began to walk back to my original post, joined by my fellow ship mates I began to shake once more as I heard the ominous drones of approaching planes began to roar out in the sky above.

I was frightened but also angry. The enemy had fired a torpedo at us in an attempt to kill us all! Were they now going to drop bombs on us as well? The anxiety, that had fleetingly melted away, was now ignited tenfold and I began to pray, once more, for mine and my comrades' survival. I looked above as the bomb doors of the German aircrafts opened and their deadly loads began to plummet down towards the sea.

The enemy planes dropped their shells but luckily, God was with us once more. The Teakwood was not struck by any of the falling bombs. Some fell so close that the vessel shook but we didn't take one hit. The ship was not broken any more than it already was by the torpedo strike. Two accompanying navy boats had been sank but I was assured that the men had been rescued and would be collected from the life rafts as soon as possible; I hoped this was true and not just a line spun to boost our morale.

The convoy limped towards England and, finally, one fresh but cold morning, after many days of uncertainty and worry I climbed onto the deck of the Teakwood. Almost immediately, I was absolutely sure I could smell the pure aroma of English soil. I heard cheering coming from the front deck and went to investigate the cause. I pushed my way to the front of the crowds and smiled widely at the wonderful sight before me.

I and every other man aboard, who saw the distant chalk from the white cliffs of Dover thanked God that we were almost home. We had survived the journey. I fought back the tears of joy when I realised that I would now hold Violet in my arms again and would meet my firstborn after all. The Teakwood limped pathetically through the water as it made its slow journey towards home.

There had been fatalities and injuries during the attack and most of the men were in a state of shock but had managed to maintain a hardy façade. We all knew, it was considered bad for morale if any man was caught complaining about his lot, it had been drummed into us on several occasions.

When the harbour master at the Dover port spotted our stricken vessel approaching, he immediately rang a loud siren to alert all who would be necessary in the rescue of the crew, of out imminent arrival. The claxon rang out loud and clear and I strained my eyes to see the flurry of activity on the dock yard.

As we neared the quay and the figures became clearer I had to fight back a sob. I was sure that death had come to visit when the enemy had launched their attack and now I felt as though I was getting a second chance at life and I meant to make the most of every minute. Finally, the Teakwood shuffled into the dock. I waited, at my post as the injured were stretchered off the vessel first followed by the poor souls that had been killed in the German attack.

Once again, I fought back tears as the Teakwood clumsily came to rest in Dover and I was not the only one. Many of my fellow sailors had tears in their eyes as they watched the bodies of our dead friends being carried up the gangplank. The war had certainly made its presence felt to all on board.

It seemed an interminably long wait as we all made our way to the shore and stood in line. After a quick de-briefing, we were ordered to pick up our kitbags and any other belongings. We were then told to climb aboard the waiting trucks to be driven to our base.

I clambered into the vehicle and as I sat I heard a loud noise that sounded like metal being crushed and I turned and looked in the direction of my ship. The poor old girl had now fallen onto her starboard side and the sea water was washing onto the decks. She looked like a big animal floundering in the waves and the sight of her struggling upset me so deeply and I felt a physical pain in my chest. It seemed to me as though I was losing one of my homes.

This ship had been my comfort and warmth for four years, almost like an old friend that you thought would be around forever, but no more. I turned and saluted the vessel as the truck lurched into motion and onto wherever the Merchant Navy decided we were going. After two long weeks back at the base I was finally given the news that I had been waiting for. I had been granted three days leave and I couldn't pack my things quick enough.

It was a particularly cold October morning in 1939 when I heaved my heavy kitbag onto my shoulder and hurried up the familiar street towards mine and Violets little cottage. The longing I felt to see Violet increased with each passing second and I actually ran the last few yards. Dumping my belonging in the narrow hallway, I walked towards the kitchen, as I was sure that was where she would be, and pushed open the door.

The sight I saw would, I was sure, stay with me for the rest of my life. There, rocking gently in the wooden rocking chair, was Violet singing to the daughter I had never met. I walked towards them and gazed down at the tiny child. I noticed that her silken, downy hair was the same colour as my own. I looked a little closer and the little child's tiny face turned towards me.

Her eyes were so startlingly like mine, it was like looking into a mirror. The love Violet obviously felt for our baby illuminated from her face and oozed from her pores. It was a startling sight and one that made me feel more determined than ever to fight against the enemy and win this war.

Violet gasped as I entered and was now grinning from ear to ear. She made to stand but I pushed her gently back into the chair. She smiled widely as she introduced me to our daughter, Hester who was now eight months old. I knelt down and put my arms around my wife and daughter, revelling in Violets familiar warmth and smell.

Both our tears of relief and joy mingled together as we rejoiced in the sight of our child and my home coming, I felt as though I couldn't take my eyes off her. I had worried that the long separation would mean that I couldn't bond with my daughter but I needn't have worried, it was love at first sight and I drank in every inch of her tiny form so I would remember it when I was aboard ship once more.

The three days we spent together were so precious. Violet and I got to know our new daughter together and cherished every single minute. It was a very intense time because we wanted to make the most of every second we could spend together. On a practical side, I made the space under the stairs more comfortable and reinforced the sides with a couple of old railway sleepers that were going begging. I needed to do everything I possibly could to ensure the safety of Violet and Hester while I was at sea and unable to protect them.

I managed to find a small crib at the back of a local second hand shop which had seen better days but I was sure Violet would clean it up a treat. I took one of the old but comfy, armchairs chair from the kitchen and also put that in the space under the stairs so Violet would have something comfortable sit on in the event of an air raid.

I felt an almost caveman-like instinct to protect my wife and daughter, even if I couldn't be with them. I ensured that the bulb was working so they wouldn't have to sit in the dark and encouraged Violet to pack a bag with everything she may need in case of an emergency.

I found it difficult to draw a line between protecting or scaring her but Violet had always had a sensible head on her shoulders and I needn't have worried. The said bag had already been prepared and was hanging on the door knob ready for use.

On my second evening of shore leave Violet encouraged me to go for a pint at my local pub. I didn't want to leave her but she insisted that I 'get out from under her feet' as she cooked the tea. As soon as I entered the Red Lion pub, I was glad that Violet had persuaded me to come. The smells and chatter were warmly comforting and the heat from the large open fire was very inviting.

I have to admit, the pint of bitter I drank tasted so very good that I had a second. This was what I missed on board ship, the comradery of all the male drinkers in a good English pub. Strangers patted me on the shoulder and asked if they could buy me a drink.

I felt very humble and refused their kindness, In all honesty I don't think I deserved it. I wasn't a fighting man, just a merchant seaman trying to feed a starving country, in my mind anyway. But my fellow drinkers thought differently and told me how grateful and proud they were of all of England's armed forces.

I got talking to a chap who had recently been called up, he asked me if I was interested in buying his newly acquired 'wireless' as he wouldn't need it where he was going. I was immediately interested but had no idea what the cost of the contraption would be. I thought it would be lovely for Violet to have some music to listen to when Hester was in bed so I nodded and said I would have a look. I watched as the man went outside the pub and returned a few minutes later carrying the wireless.

He placed it on the bar and then I watched as he took about ten minutes fiddling around with aerials and other bits and pieces. His fingers carefully twiddled a couple of shiny black knobs; he explained that he was 'tuning it in'. Suddenly, I heard voices coming from the inanimate object and was absolutely amazed; I laughed out loud and after a bit of haggling, I paid the guy £6.10.0.

I could hardly contain my eagerness when I burst into our kitchen just ten minutes, later after carrying the device the few yards home, looking as excited as a five year on his first day at school. The man accompanied back to the house and Violet watched curiously as I cleared a space on the sideboard for it.

We had agreed upon a price of 7/6 for the work of installing it and the aerial, and 5/- for the various bits and pieces that came with it. I could see immediately that this was a good quality piece of furniture. It stood in a large polished wooden case.

Although, once we had become used to it, we only ever used the two channels of the home service and the light programmes, its dial showed that it was capable of receiving broadcasts from much further afield. I was more than delighted with my purchase especially when Violet smiled and nodded her approval.

Violet and I watched as the man tuned the radio in once more. She laughed joyfully and clapped her hands in astonishment as the sounds of Gracie fields rang out of the small device. I told her the wireless would keep her company in the evenings and she hugged me gratefully. I held her close to me for a long while.

We looked into each other's eyes and I knew that Violet would be the only woman I would ever love. I knew then and there that if anything happened to her I would want no other and that night, as I lay close to her in our bed, I prayed to God that we would all survive this terrible war.

When my leave came to an end we walked to the station together. Edna, Violet's friendly next door neighbour, offered to watch Hester, who was sound asleep in her pram, so we didn't have to take her out on such a bitter cold day. We both clung onto each other as we stood on the hard, grey station platform waiting for the roar of the train engine and the belch of steam, from the funnel, when the vehicle thundered into sight.

Both of us knew it would be a long while before we saw each other again. In peacetimes this had not seemed to matter because we knew that we would eventually meet again but now, with the world at war, nothing was certain. The screech of the guards whistle indicated the train's imminent arrival and we let each other go with wretched reluctance. I climbed aboard and hastily flung my kit back into the luggage rack above. I then slid the window down.

I waved furiously out of the open window as my beautiful Violet watched the train puff away in a cloud of steam, then disappear into the distance altogether. I whispered under my breath for her and Hester to stay safe until I came home again. I also prayed to God for my survival. It seemed more important for me to stay alive now that I had a family to support but my life, like everyone else's was in the hands of an authority we could not argue with.

II

February 5 1940
VIOLET ROSENTHAL

I could feel a chill in the air as I walked back from the station
and pulled the collar of my coat closer around my neck. It
was dreary, grey day and I found myself suddenly enveloped
in a cloak of misery. I smiled as best I could when I picked up
Hester from Edna; I didn't want to share my low mood with
anyone. I didn't want my friend feeling miserable also. I wished
Len didn't have to leave so soon but there were plenty of other
women going through exactly the same as me so I should pull
myself together.

Hester was now wide awake and eagerly looking forward to a
feed. As I watched her suckle from my breast I felt a deep ache
and gnawing worry for her future. Edna made me a cup of tea
and chatted gaily about life in general. I listened and smiled,
when I should have, but I could not shake off the feeling of
impending doom.

Once Hester was fed and winded I swaddled her in her
blankets, thanked Edna and headed towards the high street to
buy groceries. I, once again, tried to mentally talk myself out of
my desolation as I turned the pram around towards the small
block of shops. I looked down on Hester as she attempted to
kick her blankets off and bent down and tucked them firmly
around her body.

This made the little madam angry and she began to scream loudly enough to rouse the dead. I reached into my pocket and retrieved her dummy then I gently placed it in her mouth. Instantly she became an angel of serenity and I couldn't help but smile.

She had Leonard's thick, black, curly hair and his full lips and the sight of his little daughter made me start to pine for him, even though he had only just left. I picked up the few bits of shopping that I needed but my heart was not in the task. I turned and headed back home, but still couldn't rid myself despondent mood. It was like a black rain cloud was hanging over my head and following me wherever I went. As I walked along the narrow pavement, on the row where I lived, I saw Edna's children playing in the street.

The rowdy young boys always seemed to be fighting over something but it all seemed to go over Edna's head. As I neared my house, Edna came out of hers, carrying her youngest boy on her hip, and shouted the 'tea' was ready, in the general direction of her four boisterous sons. They were kicking a deflated football around but when they heard their mother shout they immediately turned and piled in the door.

Edna was smoking a cigarette and the butt was covered with her bright red lipstick, she turned towards me, she had her son, Dennis resting in one hip. She looked me up and down then announced:

'Well, I ain't seen nobody looking that miserable in a long while, what's the matter Violet, you seemed alright an hour ago, have you had bad news?' I tried to muster a smile but I just couldn't, I shrugged my shoulders:

'I don't know Edna, just a touch of the blues, I reckon, I'll be my old self before you know it, I'm sure.'

Edna immediately leaned into the pram and lifted Hester out and placed her on her other hip:

'You're 'avin your tea at ours, I won't take no for an answer,' she said as she strode into her house carrying my daughter and her son with relative ease.

I parked the pram outside my front door then happily followed her inside; I didn't feel like being alone. I was feeling a deep melancholy but didn't know why. I felt a little ashamed, what did I have to feel miserable about? Poor Len was risking life and limb to keep the country fed and thousands of men and women all over the country were fighting for our freedom. Still the feeling persisted and I hated it.

Being in the crowded little kitchen was quite overwhelming. I hadn't known Edna for long but I'd quickly discovered that she was a kind and generous person. Her husband worked on the railways and was a lovely man. As Edna dished up chips and baked beans for us all I felt my mood lift and I was greatly relieved. Being miserable served no purpose and just dragged everyone around me down. It was impossible for me not to join in with all the laughter and chatter reverberating around the room.

The boys never stopped talking and the merriment and chaos echoed around the room and pinged off the walls. Edna wouldn't let go of Hester and cuddled her constantly and told me there were too many boys in her house and she longed for a little girl. I was secretly glad that I had a daughter and not five sons, I was quite sure I wouldn't be able to cope. After a couple of hours I thanked Edna and hugged her but said I must be going because I had to put Hester to bed. Edna told me to pop in anytime I needed and not to be lonely. I thanked her again and was glad to have her as a friend.

Once I had got indoors and settled Hester, I poked the fire into life and I sat down to listen to *'Woman's Hour'* on the wireless. It was a cheerful programme, talking about recipe ideas and how to get stubborn stains out of clothes. The main idea was to encourage us all to 'make do and mend' as the war would begin to take its toll on our resources and we all needed to do our bit to make everything last a little longer.

I thought of the five little boys next door and hoped that they would never have to fight in a war. Sadly, the politicians had deemed that we must fight this one and I could only hope it would be over soon and Len and I could be a family once more.

I spent as much time as I could with King Family, I would never forget how kind they had been to me when I first came to work in their shop. It was a chilly day in April and I was glad of the warmth from the fire as I sat in the cosy room behind the back of the shop. The whole family, including Mary's husband Tim, were a fussing over Hester and she loved every minute of it.

They were all overjoyed when I announced, in late February, that I thought I was pregnant again. I, myself, was not overly pleased because I thought Leonard and I had been careful, obviously not careful enough. But I was pregnant and there was nothing I could do about it but get it on with it.

When I had confided in Edna about the new baby, she had told me about something called a French letter that prevented another pregnancy happening; I intended to ask her where I could get them from. In my mind, I thought it unfair to bring children into a world at war. I had written to Leonard to tell him about the pregnancy but had heard her nothing back yet.

As I felt the stirrings of my child fluttering in my stomach I silently willed the war to be over soon. I longed for my second child to be born into a world of peace but although I hoped this would happen, I thought it unlikely.

Since war was announced the government had ordered every British citizen to carry cumbersome gas masks around with them at all times. I gladly obeyed this order because I was terrified that I would be caught up in a gas attack. Petrol was rationed in September 1939 but this did not affect me at all as I didn't drive a car. In January 1940, butter, sugar, bacon and ham were rationed and it became increasingly difficult to make a decent meal. I was pregnant, when cheese was rationed in May which meant I was lucky because I was allowed extra rations as were all women who were having babies.

One balmy evening in the middle of June, I was locking the front door just before going to bed when the unmistakable sound of the air raid siren rang out. This was the first time I had heard it since the trial one on the day war was announced and I was instantly terrified.

I hoped that it was another test run but quickly put that idea out of my mind. I wondered if it would be alright if I fetched Hester and ran next door but I decided that there was far too many people living in that house without the added burden of Hester and myself.

Instead, I raced upstairs and gently picked up my sleeping daughter and lifted her out of her cot. I was loathed to disturb her as she looked so cosy and peaceful. The wailing of the siren had not even made her flinch; she was, thankfully, a heavy sleeper. I carried her carefully down the steps and pulled open the door of the cupboard underneath the stairs.

I was immediately annoyed with myself that I had allowed it to become cluttered, once more, with old babies clothes and other unnecessary items when Leonard had spent so much of his leave making it safe for us.

In my mind, I was wondering if I should just take Hester back upstairs and hoped once more that it was a false alarm, I really wanted it to be. Even as I was thinking this through, a terrifying noise sounded high in the night sky. There was no mistaking the thundering drone of planes approaching and my terror increased tenfold.

Holding Hester in one arm, I picked up as much as the strewn clothing as I could and threw it off the chair. As the noises of the aircraft grew louder I began to tremble. Hester must have felt the sensation because she began to cry.

As soon as I had made enough room on the chair for me to sit down, I pulled and locked the door behind me, switched on the light and sat and waited. I rocked Hester and tried to talk soothingly to her but she must have sensed that everything was not well and screamed louder.

I couldn't help myself; regardless of the government posters telling us to 'keep calm and carry on' I couldn't stop my tears. They poured down my cheeks as I sniffed and sobbed, I was positive that I was about die and so was my little girl. I pulled her close against me and instantly gained a semblance of comfort from the warmth of her small body.

I realised with horror that I had not brought the gas masks with us and wondered if I should run and grab them from the top of the sideboard where I had carelessly left them along with the 'emergency bag' that Leonard and I had meticulously packed. The noise from above was now ear splitting and drowning out Hester's cries.

I held her as close to my pregnant body as I could. Going through my head, like a reel of a cine film, was the picture of

Hester, me and my unborn baby lying dead, gassed to death or blown to smithereens by a shell. The panic I felt shot through me like a lightning bolt.

I didn't know whether I should stay where I was or run for my life. I was sweating so badly I had transferred some of the dampness to Hester who was, thankfully, falling back into an exhausted sleep. When I heard the bombs dropping, it felt like the world was ending. I imagined this cramped, little room was going to become mine and Hester's tomb. I longed to feel Leonard's comforting arm around my shoulders and to smell his familiar aftershave that always made me feel safe.

I screamed loudly when a bomb dropped so near that the whole house shook Hester and I were covered in a blanket of concrete dust and I hurriedly wiped it off her tiny face. I heard glass breaking and the sound of falling masonry and all I could do was to sit and pray. I didn't know if God existed but at least it was someone to talk to as each petrifying hour dragged slowly by.

I must have dropped off to sleep at some point because I was roused by the noise of the 'all clear' as it rang loudly out. The sound startled me but I immediately calmed myself so I wouldn't disturb Hester.

I tried to shift myself into a standing position while moving as little as possible. I couldn't believe the stiffness in my limbs and found it difficult to struggle upright. I had no idea how long I had been sitting in the little room, time had seemed to stand still. Gingerly, I unlocked the door and pushed it open and was relieved to see the rest of my home was still standing. I looked at the clock on the front room side board and saw that it was five thirty in the morning.

I crept up the stairs and lay Hester gently down into her cot. I gazed at her, just joyfully happy that she and I were alive. I crept back down the narrow staircase and inspected my home for damage. As I walked from room to room I could see that everything in the house was now coated with a thick layer of dust. As I surveyed my property and tried to decide if I should start to clean up or get a few hours of sleep, I heard a quiet knock on the front door.

I opened it to see Edna standing there with her shabby dressing gown pulled around her body and curlers in her hair. She asked me how I was and I fell into her arms, sobbing, she patted my shoulder as I tried to quell the panic that threatened to rise inside me. I had spent the last ten hours pushing it back down inside of me so that I did not distress Hester.

As quickly as I could, I pulled myself together again. This wasn't the stiff upper lip that we British were supposed to show. Once I had stopped sobbing Edna came in and made us both a cup of tea. I was so grateful to her, she had a large family to take care of but, as soon as she could, she had come to check that I was alright and this meant an awful lot to me. I could tell that Edna was also shocked, her normally pink face was as white as porcelain and her hand shook as she lit a cigarette. The raid had frightened us all and caught us all unaware and unready.

I felt grateful that, at the moment, at least I only had Hester to see to. Edna had five lively boys, and it must have been difficult to ensure that they were all safe. I didn't think that the whole family could possibly fit in the small cupboard under her stairs. Edna explained that they all lay under her large iron bed, now erected in the kitchen of her home that served as a table during the day, in the hope that that would protect them from the bombs. Edna drank up and left and told me to call in later in the day, I promised I would and we hugged each other tightly before she returned to her home next door.

I knew I wouldn't be able to get any more sleep now so I set about cleaning up. Fragments of dust hung in the air. Every orifice and work top of my home was covered in grey concrete coating. Later on that morning, I put the wireless on to see what general damage Bristol had suffered in the raid, and if anyone had died, but I was surprised to hear no mention of it at all.

I supposed that, maybe; the enemy were able to listen to our news broadcasts, as well, so the attack was being kept quiet to make the German think that they had caused no carnage or death. This was the only reason I could think of.

Once I had sorted the mess I set about making the cupboard under the stairs fit for our safety. I took all the clothing and clutter out and put it in a couple of boxes which I then put underneath my bed. I then took some candles and magazines and left them on a small table beside the armchair. I took the candles in case the lightbulb didn't work and the electric went during a raid. I then washed some bedding and put it in the little crib that Leonard had bought then gave the whole place a good washing down.

Just as I was finishing up I heard the familiar voice of Hester crying for attention. I put the polish and duster in the cupboard under the sink and went to see to her. I couldn't help but smile when I gazed down at her. She was grinning widely and her bright blue eyes sparkled like stars in the night sky. She was trying to kick off her bedding while chewing on a small teddy bear that she had had since birth.

I gathered the warm, milky bundle into my arms and kissed her soft cheek. Once I fed and bathed her I decided to get a good amount of food shopping done, as much as rationing would allow. I pushed the large, carriage-built pram along with Hester sitting up looking around.

Summer had finally arrived and it was a warm day. She seemed captivated by every sight she saw along the way. My daughter was prevented from climbing out by the leather reins that were clipped to either side of the pram. Every time she saw something that she thought was interesting she pointed and shouted to make me aware of it.

I smiled at my giggling daughter but abruptly stopped when I turned the corner on the end of the street. I was absolutely stunned. I gazed at the little terrace of houses that has once stood adjacent to our street, they were no more. Only a small alley stood between the two terraces and these homes were now a mountain of cement dust and twisted masonry.

Personal possessions were on show for all, the world, to see and I felt like I was intruding into someone else life. Ragged curtains fluttered in the warm breeze, twisting around the broken panes of glass.

I remembered praying to God, as I sat in the tiny room the previous night, praying for my life and that of my daughters. I wandered if these people had been doing exactly the same but their prayers had remained unanswered. I hoped that all the residents had survived. The debris was widespread and a large area had been cordoned off.

There were still several firemen and the workers from the home guard trying to make the area safe. A gas pipe wriggled around like and angry snake as flames licked out of the top of it. Several people were trying to tie down the pipe before it set something else alight.

Broken sheets of glass littered the area and the stench of burning oil was overpowering. I moved on as quickly as the damaged pavement would allow and, to my utter shame, thanked God that it was those people that the bomb had fallen on, not me and Hester.

The raid was all everyone was talking about as I queued at the butchers and grocers to get our daily rations. To my mind, it was all guesswork as to how many had been killed because how could anyone really know when there was obviously a news black-out.

It became evident, to all I spoke to, that the phoney war we believed we were living through was now well and truly over and it was a sobering experience for me and the rest of the inhabitants of Lavender Street. Up until now, the war seemed to be happening a long way away and to other people, now it had come to my home and I was distraught.

In my mind, a mother was supposed to protect her offspring but I was powerless against a faceless enemy that attacked us when we were all asleep. I knew that anyone who was in a property that took a direct hit had little chance of survival. The thought that that could happen to Hester and she might never grow up caused a veil of sorrow to wash over me. It seemed unfair, she was just a baby.

I tried to visualise how the men fighting the enemy must feel if they were called upon to kill another human being in order to save their own life. The thought was beyond my comprehension. I imagined how frightened and disorientated they must be. One day they may have been a postman or milkman, now they were killing other men in a strange country. I could almost taste their bewilderment and fear.

I was glad that I was a woman and wouldn't be called upon to fight then I immediately felt guilty because so many men were fighting to save me and the rest of the country. I was absolutely certain that they would rather be back home, having a pint at their local and doing their everyday mundane jobs.

My own terror, last night as I sat the raid out, was so acute that it felt almost physical so how must it feel to be face to face with another human being hell bent on killing you? The thought sent a shudder down my spine and I hurried home to clean the cooker, or do anything physically tiring so it that would keep my morbid thoughts at bay. I knew it wasn't a good thing to let these things go through my head but it was difficult to dispel.

Once home, I sat Hester in the little playpen in the corner of the room then turned towards the sideboard. I leant forward and tuned in the wireless and silently thanked Leonard for the wonderful gift. As I listened to the upbeat tunes that rang out, it took my mind off the horrors of war, for a short time anyway.

It was now the beginning of July but here was still a chill in the air. I heard the front door opening and Edna, my neighbour, shouting hello. She walked into the kitchen looking very animated and excited about something:

'You'll never guess what?' she said, her eyes shining brightly in anticipation:

'Tell me,' I said grinning:

'The government want women to work, they're opening up crèches for the little ones, they want us to do the men's jobs, we'll be earning our own money, what do you think of that?' she asked as she pulled a leaflet from her apron pocket.

I was totally flabbergasted. Hester began wailing so I handed her a rusk and sat her in her playpen with her dolly:

'How are we supposed to do that, what type of work?' I asked:

'Anything from bus driving to bomb making, apparently the munitions factories is where they're paying best money, I'm off up to the factory on Charles Street tomorrow to offer my services, it's only a half hour walk, think of what we could do with our own money?'

The prospect of earning my own money, once more, was very tempting and I quickly asked Edna if I could go with her the following day. I was sure Leonard would not object to me finding myself a job especially if it would help the war effort. I was so excited about the prospect that I could hardly sleep that night as I lay and anticipated what I would spend my first week's wages on.

It was with a mixture of excitement and trepidation that Edna and I made our way to the Bristol Aeroplane Works. We had gone through a list of jobs that women were needed to do and this seemed the best one by far. It was fairly close to home, only a mile away and it had a crèche on site.

The wages seemed very good. We had both put on our best outfits to try and make a good impression on our future employer. Edna had left her older boys playing on the street but pushed her youngest son in decrepit, ancient pushchair along the uneven pavement.

I pushed large carriage pram holding a sleeping Hester along the uneven pavement. The plan was that Edna would watch

Hester while I had my interview and I would return the favour while she had hers. However, when we arrived we were told to stand in the already long queues to register for war work. Hester remained asleep throughout and I began to feel increasingly nervous. I was six months pregnant and hoped that wouldn't scupper my chances of getting a job.

The lady who sat at the desk explained that they were doing block interviews as they needed several workers to fill the vacancies left by the men away fighting. This flummoxed both Edna and I as I couldn't leave my daughter unattended and she wouldn't leave her son. The problem was solved by a matronly lady who approached and offered to take care of the children. She was well into her sixties but explained that she was in charge of the crèche and that Hester and Dennis, Edna's baby son, would be well cared while we sat through our interviews.

Before either of us had a chance to voice any doubts, she was wheeling the pram towards a long Nissan hut, while pulling the pushchair behind her, and flapping her hand at any objections we might have made. A voice yelled through a loud speaker instructing us all to go towards large aircraft hangar to the right of where we stood.

I felt a bit like I was a cow, in herd of cattle, being ushered to the milking shed. However, I did as I was told and shuffled along obediently with the rest of the crowd. When we were all inside the hangar, a large loud lady, wearing a Royal Air force uniform bellowed out, with one of the loudest voices that I had ever heard, that we should head towards the line of tables to the side of the building.

I and the rest of the women immediately obeyed the order and when we reached the tables we sat down on long narrow benches and waited as several sheets of paper were given to each woman. It seemed my pregnancy was not a barrier to me gaining employment. The factories were desperate for workers to replace the fighting men.

I looked at the long forms I had been given to fill in. Much of what I had to sign was to do with security and secrecy. The correspondence strongly emphasised the importance of telling us no one what we were doing once we had started working.

When I had answered all the questions I signed my signature then handed it to the person in charge who the same large a lady in a military uniform with the loud voice. She appeared seemingly from nowhere and began shushing all of us chattering women. She then began to speak:

'Firstly, I would like to thank each and every one of you for applying to do this valuable work. This will allow our men to concentrate on winning the war. If we are to win this war we must all pull together. The work is tedious and time consuming and the shifts are long. If you don't think that you are capable of withstanding this, now is the time to leave, we have no time for shirkers.'

She looked around the room but not one of the thirty or so ladies packed into the building left so she continued:

'Very good, you will all be issued with overalls and foot wear. No metal objects are allowed on the shop floor, including hair pins. You will all wear headscarves, covering your heads and no hair must be showing. You will wear the overalls given and nothing else, no jewellery or make up is permitted, not even wedding rings, this is for your own safety and to minimise the risk of explosions from the sections where gun powder is being used.'

She looked around to make sure that each had every one of the women were giving her our full attention, and then she began to speak once more:

'Lastly, you must not breathe a word to a soul about the nature of your work or where it is. The very nature of this business makes us a prime target for the Luftwaffe, which is why it is so very important that loose lips must be silenced. Now Ladies, thank you for listening, please head towards the far end of the building to collect you overalls and shift sheets.'

Then she was gone and we all began to chatter excitedly before walking to where she had told us to co. I collected everything I needed and then Edna and I made our way towards the door. Both of us chatted excitedly about starting our new jobs and how proud we were that we were doing something towards the war effort. The money would come in very handy also, with two little mouths to feed. I couldn't wait to write and tell Len that I now had a job and could support myself. I knew he would be proud I was doing my bit and I was too.

The war continued bringing gloom and destruction to the many hard working people living in Great Britain. My days passed relatively quickly. Bringing up my little girl was hard work but also very rewarding and soon I would have two lives relying on me. It could also be a little isolating so I enjoyed the company of my fellow factory workers when I was doing my shifts.

I was satisfied that my daughter was being well cared for. It was the long, dark evenings that were the problem, I missed having adult company, someone who I could talk to about my day and the little things that Hester had done that made me smile…or grimace.

Sometimes, when I was not on the nightshift at work, the dark evenings would draw in and I felt as though I was suffocating in my own loneliness. The blackout curtains only succeeded in making me feel all the more hemmed in and alone. I kept myself as busy as I could to stave off any morbid feelings but sometimes it was hard not to let my imagination run away with me and wonder what would happen if the Germans won the war.

In October 1940, I gave birth to my second daughter, Daisy, who looked like a carbon copy of her older sister. I was frightened at how I would cope with two young children but Edna, as usual, was as good as gold and on hand when I needed help. Also Mary Dunstan and her mother, Mrs King, were regular visitors and I regarded them and Edna as the family I had never had.

I knitted socks for our fighting men and kept the house spotlessly tidy but sometimes I found myself having an imaginary conversation with myself about nothing much. I tried not to think about the danger Len was in every day. Each crossing he made was now fraught with danger and I hoped he was managing to cope with his once peaceful world being shattered by the war.

Sadly, I was sure that there were many other wives in the same boat as me. All our men were scattered who knows where and we didn't have a clue when they would come home. Every time a letter with familiar writing landed on the door steps, our hearts would soar with joy at the simple form of communication with our loved one. All we could do was hope that we all survived this wretched war and our families could be all together again soon.

12

October 12 1940
MICHAEL ROSENTHAL

Living in Ireland made the war seem a long way away. I wanted to pretend that it was not happening and just wallow in my cosy life with Lucy. We had been married for eighteen months earlier and now lived in the cottage next to Auntie Gerta where Lucy's parents had lived before they died within two weeks of each other some years ago. It was an idyllic life, living and working among the lush green fields and the clean Irish air.

The only thing missing in our lives was a child but I conceded that Lucy and I were only young and had plenty of time to start a family. I still missed my parents enormously but now that I had Lucy I found things easier to cope with. I could now think of my mother and father and remember the good times and not be overwhelmed with sadness. The picture of them being beaten no longer haunted but dreams and was replaced by visions of happier times.

Life went on in its orderly routine but as much as I tried to bury my head in the sand and pretend the war was not happening, I could not ignore the terrible news on the radio and in the newspapers. The horrors that were unfolding in the city of my birth were too terrible for me to contemplate. Very little was said about the bombing of English cities but everyone was aware that it was happening. The devastating news was spread, in hushed tones, by word of mouth from people who had visited the battered and beleaguered places.

I still grasped at a small morsel of hope that my mother and father were safe and well. I wanted to believe that they had found somewhere safe to hide until the war was over but in my heart of hearts I doubted that was true. Auntie Gerta had spent years looking for them but each search had come to a dead end. In reality, I held little hope for their survival.

In mid-October 1940, I decided that I could hide no more. The news was broadcast that my fellow Jews were being herded into labour camps and England, the country that had offered me and Lucy sanctuary when we badly needed it, was still being relentlessly bombed by the enemy. I was relieved when I explained my need to do my bit to Lucy and Gerta, and they both understood and agreed that it was the right thing to do. Although I knew they were right, it wasn't without apprehension that I boarded the boat from Ireland to Holyhead just two weeks after I had made my decision.

Later in life, I regarded the serene journey across the glassy water as one of the last times I had ever felt completely at peace with life. I caught a train to Southampton and that was one of the biggest thrills of my life. I felt such excitement as I leant out of the small train window looking out at the steam belching from the massive black funnel and listening to the whistle screaming as the engine roared into life.

It felt, to me, as though, I was a child once more and I couldn't help grinning as the vehicle chugged and puffed its way out of the station. I finally arrived at my destination and watched, sadly, as the train continued with its journey.

On arrival I asked one of the station porters how I should go about enlisting and he explained where I needed to go. I followed his instructions and found myself standing in front of a building that looked like it used to be a school or a library. I drew nearer then saw the large sign saying 'recruiting office'. I entered the building hesitantly as I was not sure which direction I was supposed to go in. My dilemma was quickly solved by a man, sitting behind a desk a few yards in front of me, bellowing for me to approach him.

I did so immediately. The stripes on the shoulder of his military uniform and the tone of his voice told me that he was not a man to be ignored. I explained that I had come across from Ireland to enlist but that I was originally from Germany but was Jewish. I told him about my families' flight and he listened with interest and what might have been a semblance of pity. I couldn't tell and didn't really want to talk about a chapter of my life that I would rather forget. I was aware that he needed to know my origins so I told him the shortest story I could.

He gave me some paperwork which I duly filled in and handed back. I was then sent to another room which had at least twenty men of similar age to me all looking a little bewildered but at the same time determined. We all waited for our next order. The process of enlisting took a lot less time than I thought it would. After filling in the paperwork I was given a medical exam which I passed with flying colours. I was told to find a place to stay for the night and to return in the morning. I would then be told where I was being sent for my basic training and then onto where I would be based.

I was lucky enough to find a clean and descent room to rent upstairs, in a lodging house, three doors up from the train station. The room smelt of disinfectant and polish and the owners had made it as homely as they could. Once I had unpacked my belongings, I sat down to write to Lucy, Gerta and Len to tell them what had happened once I had arrived on the mainland.

I expressed my relief at passing my medical exam though I'm not sure why because I felt as fit as a fiddle so there was no reason I shouldn't be given a clean bill of health. I wrote that I was being sent to an army training camp the following day. This done, I sealed the envelopes and walked along the street to post them.

I then walked along the road to stretch my legs after my long journey and the time I had spent in the recruiting office. I found a small but charming little pub a few miles from my lodgings where I bought a delicious meal. I also enjoyed the pint of bitter I drank with it, even if it tasted a tad watered down. I sat and looked out of the window at the people of Southampton who were going about their business as usual. They seemed unperturbed that their country was at war but I had no idea of how they actually felt deep inside.

I wondered how they coped when an air raid occurred and they had to listen to the bombs raining down on the city hoping they would land on someone else. It had turned out to be a relatively warm evening and I enjoyed the walk back to my room. I wanted to get an early night to ensure I was up bright and early the following morning. Just as I reached my lodgings a dark cloud obliterated the evening sun and I felt a cold shiver run through my body. I did not know then that this would be one of the last times I would feel peace on English soil.

My alarm roused me and I was momentarily stunned not to find Lucy lying in bed beside me before I quickly realised where I was. I swung my legs out of the single, iron-framed bed and made my way to the wash stand in the corner of the room. I dressed quickly and refused my landladies offer of breakfast. I was feeling nervous and my churned up stomach wouldn't hold food well. I joined one of the queues of men that were snaking their ways around the recruiting office. Finally, it was my turn and I was given my papers that would tell me where I would spend the next six weeks.

Getting to the training camp on the far outskirts of the city was a feat in own rite. It was only a short journey, with very few stations to pass through to get my base but nonetheless a difficult one. None of the stations were signposted. All the signs had been removed to flummox the Germans, if they invaded England. The only way to find out exactly what station I had actually arrived at was to ask the station master.

Without exception, at each stop, first I was met with suspicion and asked probing questions about why I needed to know. It was not until I showed them my enrolment papers that they were happy to depart the information to me. It seemed that every man in the country was on the lookout for enemy spies and that made me feel part of a wider community that would hopefully help us win this war.

To add to this, the constant shelling from the enemy, on the beleaguered city, had caused a lot of damage to the railways. This made the journey more hazardous still, due to the condition of the tracks and the fact that every vehicle had to adhere to the black out, so, as another evening approached, we travelled in complete darkness. The widespread blackness was stifling and terrifying. It seemed as though it was crushing my body, almost as if it meant to smother me.

I was very relieved to find that the rhythm of the train had lolled me to sleep and when I woke, a beautiful sunrise was edging its way over the horizon. It was penetrating through the grey damp dawn like a beacon of hope. I took that as a sign that I had made the right decision to fight for England. I shook my head to wake myself properly then lit a woodbine and began to relax for the remainder of the journey. From a few carriages along I could hear the sound of voices singing. I craned my neck to listen and could hear the somewhat flat tones of the song '*pack up your troubles in your old kit bag*'

I didn't know the words but I hummed along to the tune. Without knowing why, I felt as though I needed to be with the people who were singing. I was aware we had a united task ahead and the future of the country depended on all of us who had enlisted. As I rose and headed towards the noise, I realised my chest was puffed with patriotism and I was very proud of myself and ready for whatever faced me in the coming months. I entered the carriage where the singing was coming from and sat in a corner seat and immediately began singing along to the next song, feeling very much part of a band of brothers.

I continued singing my heart out, the more songs we all sang the louder we got. As we began a raucous rendition of '*It's a long way to Tipperary*', I thought I could hear a low, growling noise in the skies above but it was barely audible so I dismissed it as something in my imagination. The noise of the men on the train was now deafening with some of them banging on the tables and others stamping their feet in time with the beat. I strained my ears and tried to peer out of the small carriage window.

I was now pretty sure that I could hear the low droning noise of planes somewhere in the distance above me. I tried to tell myself that I was imagining the sound because no one else around me seemed to have heard it. Then, without noise or warning, I saw a vivid blue flash mushroom its way towards me and my world turned black. I have no idea how much time had passed when I gradually began to regain control of my senses. Very slowly, I became aware that I was lying in a cramped space.

I could feel pain but could not yet register where it was coming from. I tried to move but couldn't. Something was crushing me and I slowly came to realise the agony I was feeling was in my feet. It began to hurt excruciatingly so I made a superhuman effort to free myself from whatever was pinning me down. I then tried to focus on my surroundings. With horror, I suddenly realised that my feet were on fire. Freeing my body now became easier as I watched the flames licking at my boots.

The smell of the burning rubber of my footwear, together with human hair and skin seemed to inject me with herculean strength and throw aside anything that was stifling my movement. Once I was free from my restraints, I leant forward and began banging furiously at the flames around my feet in effort to douse the fire.

I spotted a discarded tunic and grabbed it, without a moment's hesitation and pressed against my blazing feet until, finally, the fire was out. The excruciating pain, however, remained and I took deep breaths in an effort to make my mind focus on something else.

I shook my head to try and clear the grogginess that still buzzed around my mind. The picture before me was now becoming clearer. I realised, and was stunned with horror, to see that the weight pinning me down was the bodies of several dead soldiers. I felt as though I had fallen asleep and had woken up in a real life nightmare. I had never seen so many dead and mutilated bodies in one place. It was as though I was in hell.

Black, acrid smelling smoke now began to fill the carriage. I knew I had to get out if I didn't want to join my dead comrades. I couldn't walk, the pain in my feet was too great, and I could only crawl. I pulled my handkerchief from my pocket and held it over my nose and mouth as the smoke got thicker and began to sting my throat. Mercifully, as I edged further along the carriage, the fumes became thinner and less suffocating.

I clambered over many dead bodies in my bid for freedom. It was not what I wanted to do but I conceded that their time in this world was over and there was nothing I could do to help them so I must help myself. When it felt as though I could drag myself no further I was newly invigorated when I saw a dim shaft of light ahead and felt fresh air on my face.

I pulled myself upwards through a gap, made by a broken carriage window, and began screaming for help. I could see the train was lying on its side like an enormous injured animal splayed across the tracks. I saw grainy figures rushing towards me and felt myself being dragged out, away from the smoke and heat.

I have no recollection of what happened next but I woke to find myself lying on the station platform. The hard concrete was uncomfortable and dug into my back. My throat felt as though it was on fire and I tried to make some sort of sound to find out what had happened but no noise came from my mouth, I was desperate for a drink of water but the whole scene was one of chaos and destruction.

I looked down and I realised that both my hands and feet were bandaged along with the lower part of my legs. My clothing was badly singed and I couldn't help thinking how, a few days ago, I had steadfastly polished my boots to make them gleam. I wanted the army to know I was proud to be a part of it, by keeping arriving well dressed and in pristine condition. Now, most of my buttons had been ripped off and the ones that remained were smoke blackened and hanging on by a thread.

With some difficulty I pulled myself into a sitting position and tried to gesture to anyone, as my need to pour water on my burning throat was now overwhelming. Finally, a kindly old lady, wearing a WRVS uniform, saw my plight. She knelt gently beside me and held a cup to my lips. I wanted to gulp the liquid but she advised me to take it slowly and it was pure heaven to feel the cooling liquid sliding down my throat.

I put my hand up to signal that I had drunk enough. The woman then placed a rough blanket over my body; I hadn't realised that I was shivering until she did this. She then placed a cushion behind my head, patted my hand soothingly then went away to offer comfort to one of the other injured people that lay on the railway platform. There were many injured people in need of help and I wished that I could do something but a weakness seemed to have enveloped my body and I could only sit and watch,

I slowly turned my head and could see that one half of the train was leaning on its side and other half of it was completely obliterated, there was nothing left of the carriage I had sat in before I moved to join in with the patriotic singsong. This half of the train was a mess of twisted burning metal and broken glass.

It had turned into a blackened shell that was now the tomb of many poor souls. Further along the line I could see the shrouded bodies of some of the unfortunate people who hadn't made it. The sheets that covered them were stained with blood and battered limbs poked out from underneath.

I listened to the chattering going on around me and realised that the train had been bombed by the Germans. I heard that there were very few survivors and anyone who got out alive was lucky. I didn't feel fortunate as I watched the rescue teams lift the broken bodies from the belly of the train. Most of these were charred beyond recognition and only the size of the corpse indicated if the body was that of an adult or child. Some of the dead were limbless and headless. Those who did have any remaining facial features were twisted in terror.

I knew then that, for the rest of my life, I would never forget the horrific scene before me. I wanted to close eyes my but some gruesome, warped interest kept me watching. Dusk was almost upon me when I was finally lifted onto a stretcher and hoisted into the back of an ambulance. I wanted to believe that my nightmare was over but, in truth, it was only just beginning. Later, in life, I would come to realise that there are only so many repulsions the human body and mind could witness before it began to shut down and try to escape from life.

13

October 22 1940
VIOLET ROSENTHAL

Although I enjoyed my job, I still found it difficult to hand over my precious children to complete strangers. Although I had every faith in the crèche workers capabilities while minding my daughters, they still weren't me and Hester didn't really know them. The staff members at the nursery were organised but also brusque.

I suppose this was a good idea as it didn't allow mothers, like me, to brood and fuss. My daughters were whisked away before each of my shifts and I was ushered out of the door as quickly as possible. I hoped my girls realised that I didn't want to leave them but felt I had little choice. It saddened me greatly to be separated from my two week old baby, Daisy, but it was not my decision to make. Everyone in the country was expected to *pull their weight* and I was no exception.

As well as the overalls and rubber boots we were also issued with, we were also given a dull coloured brown scarf which we had to turn into a turban. We were told many times the importance of keeping our hair out of the way and off out faces.

This proved a little bit difficult for me as we were not allowed to use hair grips, in case the metal came in contact with any gunpowder, from the ladies working further down in the shed and caused an explosion. My hair had always been naturally unruly and with a mind of its own.

It constantly tried to fight its way out of the restricting head scarf and I was forever poking it back underneath in an effort to abide by the rules. Still, when I looked in the mirror during my tea break, rebellious tendrils had made their way out and would be curling around my turban as though they were trying to make their escape.

On our first day Edna and I had been shown to the large factory where we would be working. I recalled how nervous I was as the overworked supervisor pushed open the large doors and we were met with a scurrying hive of activity. There were long tables standing in rows as far as I could see. Women, and some men, of all ages were sitting at them picking up tiny metal parts and fitting them intricately together.

I remember feeling in awe of these wonderful people. I couldn't wait to start work but felt I would never reach the expert standard that these people had already achieved. Their deft fingers worked with such speed, it was almost as though they were robots. Deep concentration was etched into the lines of their faces as they made double sure that the work they did was absolutely correct. Edna and I followed the supervisor down the long room, winding our way between the tables.

We were taken to a bench at the far end and we quickly familiarised with our co-workers. They, in turn, gave us a brief nod. We were told that formal introductions would take place when we were on one of our breaks. The lady who was going to teach me my job was called Susan Bromley and, although was a good few years older than me, we hit it off right away and were soon getting on like a house on fire.

She patiently showed me how to assemble the aeroplane parts and stressed how important it was to get it right and told me I must ask her if I felt I couldn't understand any aspect of the job. She was patient and kind and we quickly became firm friends. She made me feel confident that I was capable of doing my work and my nerves quickly vanished as I concentrated on the job in hand.

To our initial disappointment, Edna was placed at another end of a long table at the other end of the room and was going to be being taught her craft by a middle aged lady. We had hoped that we would be working together but, as it was, we just got on with things as we were supposed to. Edna was wearing bright red lipstick as usual. The supervisor did not reprimand her so I decided the 'no make-up' rule wasn't strictly adhered to. It made a stark contrast to our drab workwear and grubby surroundings.

At first, I was positive I would never be able to get the hang of fitting the aeroplane parts together but, with Susan's endless explaining and help, by the time the dinner bell rang, I felt like an old hand.

As the noise echoed around the room I watched as everyone downed tools and headed towards a doorway to the left of our work benches. Susan beckoned me to follow her and I quickly put down my work and walked along behind her. We walked down a corridor then turned into an enormous canteen with several long tables in two columns down the length of the room.

Right away I felt the atmosphere was one of comradery and friendship and I was certain I had made the right decision to take this job, even if I did miss my girls. I told myself that at least I got to see them at the end of my shift, unlike Len, who missed out on seeing them for months at a time.

We queued for our food, which was steak and kidney pudding, mashed potato, cabbage and watery gravy. I was so hungry that I didn't notice the lumps in the mash or the limp cabbage; it tasted like a veritable feast to me and I wolfed it down. Once we had finished eating, we all drank weak tea and Susan introduced me to her friend Joyce.

I estimated Joyce to be very young, around seventeen or eighteen years old. She had a youthful, playful type of personality. Her blonde hair coiled around her head scarf in little golden wisps as her blue eyes shone as she spoke about her 'date' that evening.

Joyce explained, animatedly that her boyfriend has managed to borrow a car and he was going to drive her into Clifton and treat her to a slap up meal. Being naturally cynical, I wondered what the man would want in return for the food but Joyce's enthusiasm was infectious and I soon joined in the conversion about what she would wear and who she could borrow some shoes or jewellery from. Britain was at war and Joyce should take every opportunity to enjoy herself whenever she got the chance, none of us knew if we would still be alive tomorrow.

Susan broke into my thoughts by patting my shoulder and I turned in her direction. She pulled some tiny photos from her overall pocket and showed me pictures of her daughters, Edith and Iris. She was a little tearful as she spoke about them and I understood her sadness.

She explained that they had been evacuated to Cornwall in July of 1940 and Susan missed them constantly. It was not easy leaving our children to be brought up by family or strangers but we knew it had to be done if we were going to help Britain win this war. Susan explained that she felt she had no choice but to evacuate her precious children.

I listened as she explained how she had kept them with her until May 1940. But one day, when they were both at school, the enemy attacked and there was a daytime air raid which was quite unusual. Normally the enemy liked to attack as night when we were all tucked up in our beds, hopefully trying to catch us unawares.

When the air raid siren rang out it's warning, on this particular day, the children and their teachers all raced to the concrete shelter some way from the school. When the all clear sounded Susan raced out of the factory to her daughter's school and came across a place of total devastation.

Susan wept as she explained that the school was no more and the shelter was buried under a pile of rubble. I put my arm around her shoulders as the memory of the awful day came back to her and made her tremble. She told me how she stood helplessly, as the rescuers pulled at the rubble with their bare hands. It was two hours later when Susan discovered her children were injured but alive. Edith, Susan eldest, was the last to be pulled from the shelter.

As she was dragged out, the building collapsed killing the teachers inside and some of the rescuers. Susan explained that it was then that she realised she was being selfish keeping the girls with her and in constant danger so she took them to Carmarthen Farm, where her husband's parents lived. Her husband, Edward was away fighting in France and Susan missed her family very much. I understood but I didn't think that I could ever let another person bring up Hester and little Daisy, family or not, and I prayed to God that I would not have to.

We filed back to work once the hooter had sounded indicating that the dinner break was over. The afternoon flew by; I had focused so hard on doing my job correctly that I hardly noticed the time passing. I clocked out then walked briskly over to nursery to collect Hester and Daisy.

I half expected Hester to be miserable and sullen, because I had left her in a strange place. To my surprise, the opposite happened and she was smiling widely and telling me she didn't want to leave. Daisy, the nursery staff told me, had been a model baby and a pleasure to take care of.

I was feeling happy and contented as I headed back to my cosy cottage with the two girls in the large carriage pram. I was a little 'put out' that my daughters had not missed me but told myself to stop being silly and be thankful instead. Even though the world was at war I felt strangely peaceful and in charge of my own destiny. It was a heady feeling to be earning my own money once more and an added bonus was that Edna and I were also helping towards the war effort.

I hoped it wouldn't last long and that Len would be home soon and we could be a little family once more. I tried not to think about the dangers his job entailed. I was now so busy with working and raising my daughters that I had little time to dwell on the scariness of the world and that could only be a good thing. By the time I fed and bathed Hester and Daisy I was absolutely exhausted. I could barely eat my own meal before I trudged up the stairs and fell into my bed.

14

November 3 1940
MICHAEL ROSENTHAL

I spent many months in hospital having the burns to my feet and legs dressed and bandaged on a daily basis to fight off the threat of infection. The treatment felt sometimes as if it was more painful than the injuries but I endured it with a little fuss as I could. I knew that I should be grateful that I had escaped the train crash with my life, whereas so many others had perished. The burns on my hands were healing well and I had no broken bones. Only eleven people on the packed train had lived through the raid and I was one of those.

Although, I now realised how lucky I was to have survived, the burnt and twisted bodies I witnessed in the aftermath of the bombing haunted my waking hours and intruded into my dreams. I was relieved, when I was finally considered ready for release from the confines of the hospital. Too much sitting around gave me too much time to think and I needed other distractions to keep my mind occupied. I had no visitors as any unnecessary travel was restricted throughout the war as the transport military personnel took precedence over any other itinerants.

I was finally signed out of the hospital. I was provided with a travel pass so I could go back home to recuperate and get myself back to full fitness. I truly believed the serenity and calm of Ireland would help heal my mind and body. As soon as I was able to walk unaided, I filled my flask with tea and tramped around the countryside armed with my trusty binoculars. I loved watching the many different species of birds going about their daily lives.

I never tired of watching the mother birds build the nest that would eventually be a home for their chicks. They worked tirelessly to ensure their offspring were fed and safe, without complaint, and I felt very humbled by their selfless act.

I was constantly amazed at the many different breeds of bird the soared around the blue skies of Donegal. Lucy sometimes came with me but she was easily bored and it didn't surprise me in the slightest when she would find some excuse to return home after less than half an hour. Secretly, I was happier with just myself and the wildlife.

I loved Lucy with every fibre of my being but I also knew she was used to getting her own way. Before she had become pregnant she had been thoroughly cossetted and spoiled by aging parents. She now expected Gerta and me to pander to her needs in the same way as they had done and we did our best to do this. It was no chore for either of us. Gerta loved Lucy as though she was her own daughter and I was glad they would have each other for company when I eventually left for war once more.

I was deemed fit for combat in late March 1941. I, once again, bid a tearful goodbye to Lucy and Gerta. I caught the ferry to the mainland once again. My arrival at my designated base seemed a long time coming and I was eager to get on with the business of winning the war.

I was issued with a new uniform and kit. That evening I donned my new uniform then stood, in my barracks, looking at myself in them mirror. I was very proud to see a serving soldier staring back at me and I vowed to do my very best for Britain. I completed three weeks of intensive training and spent the next seven months fighting to defeat the Italian 'Regia Marina' which was off the Peloponnesus, on the coast of Greece in the Battle of Cape Matapan.

In December 1941 and I found myself aboard a troop ship destined for Malaya. The speed at which my posting had come about took my breath away and I didn't feel entirely ready for the task ahead. I talked to my fellow soldiers and was glad to hear that it was widely thought our posting was a good one. It was deemed by top brass a relatively safe destination as the war had not yet reached this corner of the earth and it was our job to prevent it doing so.

I enjoyed my time aboard ship. The lapping of the waves and the salty air helped cleanse my mind of the horrible images I had seen on the train and by the time the ship docked at a port in southern Malaya I felt ready for what lay ahead of me. It was as though the serenity of the ocean had given me time to prepare myself for the new challenges ahead of me. I looked ahead as the ship sailed into port and was immediately taken by the beauty of the country we were approaching.

The majestic hillsides stood above the city as though they were protecting them and the lush green trees swayed in the cooling wind. I now wished I had brought my binoculars because I spotted several species of bird that I did not recognise. I resigned myself to the fact that I would just have to make do without unless there were shops in the vicinity that sold anything similar. The sky was a vibrant blue with no clouds spoiling the wondrous colour. As I strained my eyes to gaze into the distance the whole country seemed to be an oasis of calm.

The ship had reached Chittagong, just over the Burmese border into India about six weeks after we had left Southampton. Unbeknown to me and the rest of the crew, the Japanese had already began their invasion of Malaya by the time we docked in January 1942 and we would be greatly shocked when we learned the true state of the country in the coming weeks. As it was, ignorance was bliss, and when the shipped eventually docked we were all eager to go out and explore the foreign land.

However, I later learned from more knowledgeable ship mates, that Chittagong not where we would be stationed for long. Our eventual destination was Singapore. This was roughly eighteen hundred miles from Burma, across the Gulf of Thailand. First, we were told, that we were going to make our way from Chittagong to Burma which was situated less than a hundred miles away. We would be heading for a stronghold and would help protect the Burmese from enemy invasion. I looked around the unknown city as I disembarked with the rest of my crew.

The sergeant duly informed us all that our mode of transport, to take the us hundred or so miles to our terminus, was to be a lorry crate; I turned and took sneaky glance inside the vehicle and imagined how a sardine must feel compacted in a tin can. At first, the plan was to travel straight away but then we were happily informed that we all had a twenty four hour leave before our journey was to commence.

Excitedly, a group of us decided to visit the city while we were here. We came across the *Chandanpura* Mosque which was located just beside the *Shiraj Ud Dowla* Road, which was situated in the old part of the Chittagong. We all stood gazing at the amazing building before us. It was a four storey structure with intricate decoration and bridges leading from one turret to the next. To me, it looked like a fairy tale castle, one that I'd seen in Hansel and Gretel, a child's storybook I had read as a young boy.

The complexity of the design made me think it had taken someone many years to design and build. I felt an inner feeling of peace and serenity as I gazed at the wonderful building and hoped I could revive that feeling if I ever needed it, in the future.

The following day, I and the rest of my comrades in arms, stood to attention. Each man was given a mosquito net and a small pack containing a blanket and a few toiletries. We then boarded the lorry taking us to our final destination, for the coming months anyway. The journey took around six hours and was one I'd rather not take again; it was everything I imagined it was going to be, sweltering hot, cramped and generally uncomfortable. I was relieved when we reached our journey's end.

My relief, however, turned to dismay when I viewed the conditions we were expected to live in. At first glance, the camp seemed like a run-down chanty town. There were not enough camp beds for all the men and it was a case of first come first serve. My platoon had arrived far too late to bag a bed so we had to make do with the hard, unforgiving ground. I quickly realised that the mosquito net I has been given was a Godsend. I was very lucky to have it, not everyone had been issued with this necessary piece of equipment.

Mosquitos were the direct cause of malaria which was rife throughout the camp and the net was a brilliant from of protection against the insects. The nurses and doctors seemed to be struggling to keep the infection under control without adequate medicines or hospital tents and personnel.

I wondered why top brass had not considered that this deadly disease could immobilise a whole army and had not set out a plan of action to minimise the spread of it. I saw at least ten men die from the merciless disease so guarded my mosquito net as if it were a watery oasis in a burning dessert.

Dysentery was also a very unwelcome visitor. This debilitating illness could sap the energy from a man and make him want to give the fight up to live altogether. I again wandered why the government were not taking adequate care of its fighting forces. How could they expect us to defend a country when many of the troops were weakened or killed by illness?

There was also a daily struggle with sanitation. A rancid smell emanated from the lavatory block day after day. Flies constantly buzzed around it and water was in short supply. The heat was almost unbearable as sun turned into a blurred golden ball in the sky and seemed to make the landscape quiver in the distance.

The nights, however, were a totally different kettle of fish and the first night spent at camp was awake up call for every man who arrived. If I expected it to be a cooling relief from the heat of the day I was quickly proved wrong. It was actually so icily cold that the one blanket we had been issued was not up to the job of keeping us warm. I could not believe the stark contrast between the day and night time temperatures.

I thought I'd might get some relief from the heat when

the monsoon season came along but I was wrong once again, this was new type of discomfort altogether. The rain poured endlessly from a leaden sky and there was nowhere we could go to get dry. We slept in our drenched clothing and it dried on our bodies as we slept. I began to loath the country and longed to be back in Ireland, tramping the hillside and watching the wildlife.

To my mind, I felt that the government had not made a good job when they had packed off their troops to a foreign country. The whole operation was mismanaged at best and shoddy work at worst. I didn't think that the British army could be at its fighting best with lack of water, deadly diseases and inadequate hygiene everywhere we went. When I talked to my comrades in the long, quickly cooling evenings, I found that we were all badly despondent about the conditions we were forced to live in and worried about our ability to fight.

The general consensus was that we felt as though we were the forgotten army. We rarely received any Red Cross parcels and letters from home and I wasn't sure why this was as the country was, at the moment, at peace. I could only hope that Lucy was writing to me and that at some point her letters would reach me. I had written many to her and took them to the communications post but I had no way of knowing if she received them. I could only hope that she had and that we weren't truly the forgotten army, at least by our loved ones.

15

The routine of my life didn't change much. On the days that I was working at the factory, I would prepare the evening meal the day before I left. I got used to dropping Hester and Daisy off at the nursery and was happy because Hester chattered non-stop about how much she enjoyed being there.

Daisy was now four months and I couldn't believe how quickly the time had flown by. I loved to look into Daisy's deep blue eyes as I sat nursing her in the rocking chair next to the AGA. It was precious part of motherhood that nothing could replace. Hester adored her tiny sister and tried to share her toys with her. Little Daisy was too young to notice and this frustrated Hester a bit but she was a placid child who usually went on to amuse herself, as she always had done.

It was a cold and grey February day and I had been employed at the factory for around six months. I loved the independence of making my own money but I still missed Len desperately. Luckily my work meant I had less time to dwell on his where-abouts and safety.

Our correspondence, I know, was our lifeline. Len would tell me all about where he was sailing but most of this was censored by the government in case the letters got into enemy hands. I could make a rough guess though, due to his descriptions of the places and hoped he was safe.

I, in turn, kept him updated about my job and both our daughter's development. It was sad that he was missing out on their growing up but there was nothing to be done. I sent him photos whenever possible so at least he could see what they looked like.

On this particular day, midway through the morning shift, the air raid siren screeched into life, startling me so much I almost fell off my stool. Daytime raids were a rarity, at the time, and none of us were expecting it. Even so we filed quickly but quietly down the uneven concrete steps to the damp cellar below the building.

I felt a chill go through me as I made my way towards one of the narrow benches that were lined along the walls of the building. The place was dimly lit by a few bulbs and there was little comfort to be found in our sanctuary.

Susan, Joyce and I huddled closely to each other to counteract the cold and the fear we were all feeling. For the first time, since they had been born, I wished Hester and Daisy were not in Bristol but in a place of safety and I mouthed a silent prayer to God to watch over them. When I heard the burr of the planes approaching, my heart began to pound. I would never get used to that feeling of terror that reverberated around my insides every time I heard that ominous noise. I made an enormous effort to calm my inner turmoil because I knew it would not help anyone around me if I became hysterical.

At first, the explosions sounded a long way off and, for that small mercy, I was glad. I did, however, realise that some other poor soul was taking the brunt of Hitler's wrath. The lights in the cellar flickered and occasionally went out, plunging the place into darkness and causing more terror to our already tense bodies.

It seemed like much longer but after around an hour or so the earth shattering blasts ceased and I began to breath more easily. I was sure that anytime soon the all clear would ring out and we could all resume our working day. I waited patiently as I realised it was almost lunch time and my stomach was grumbling for food.

The sound was so quiet at first that I hardly heard it. It started as a quiet buzzing, shrieking kind of sound then the noise accelerated until it reached a screeching crescendo. I was puzzled at first because this was not the all clear siren that I was expecting to hear. I could also hear the grating, growling noise of an aeroplane overhead that was struggling to stay airborne. As the noise grew louder, I covered my ears with my hands and looked around in a mad panic; everyone else in the room had the same expression on their faces.

I couldn't stop the sobs escaping as realisation hit me in the face and I was now positive that a stricken air craft was hurtling down towards us. The noise was deafening and I put my head in my lap and covered my head. I had no idea if this would save me but I felt the need to do something. I couldn't bear the thought of my daughters growing up without me. As the noise grew loud enough to blow out my ear drums I begged God to let my death be swift and painless then buried my head further into my lap.

I must have lost consciousness because at first, I thought I could hear the continuous humming of a bee but the noise gradually grew louder and I slowly opened my eyes and realised the buzzing was inside my head. I tried to remember where I was but when I turned my head to look around I was almost over coming by the throbbing agony in my temple. Slowly my eyes became used to the semi darkness.

I could just about make out the shapes of other people in the cellar. As I tried to recall what had happened a single bulb shone into life illuminating the whole place. Someone had managed screw it back into a fixing in the ceiling. I found myself propped against a wall. My head hurt and when I lifted my fingers and touched it, I felt hot, sticky blood and nausea engulf me. I put my head gently to one side and was sick.

I watched, though blurry eyes, as Susan wearily made her way over to me. She had given birth to her son, Johnny, just four weeks ago and I knew she would be worried as worried about him as I was about Hester and Daisy. I wanted to speak to her and try and reassure her that he would be fine but the words wouldn't come out, I must have been stunned by the blow to my head. She knelt down beside me and rubbed my shoulder and explained that help was on the way and that some of the men were speaking to the rescuers through a tiny hole in the rubble.

Susan asked me how I was and I finally manged to mumble that I was fine apart from a bit of a sore head. She asked if she could bring Joyce to sit with me. Susan explained that Joyce was panicking at being trapped in such a compact space and thought she couldn't breathe. I told it was fine, I hoped that looking after Joyce might take my mind off the pounding in my head.

Susan sat Joyce down next to me and I felt the poor girl's terrible trembling as I pulled her body closer to mine. I told her to take, long, deep breaths and assured her that we would be out in no time. Joyce's shuddering eased a little and I wished there was more I could do to calm her. I took a look around me now that I was feeling a little more alert. One half of the large cellar was completely destroyed. In its place was a pile of masonry, broken wood and what looked like part of the wing of a plane.

I wondered what had happened to the people on that side of the room but chose not to think about it for the present moment. I needed to concentrate on getting out alive and not ponder what had happened to those that may have already perished. As my head throbbed, Hester and Daisy came into my mind once more and I was suddenly petrified. The nursery was not far from the factory and they only had to Anderson shelters to protect the children and staff. What if they had not made it to the shelter?

Now it was my turn to feel as though I couldn't breathe. My mind would not allow me to comprehend the thought that my daughters might be dead. How would I tell Len, I couldn't possibly put it in a letter, neither could I wait until his next leave. I was tortured by the realisation that, if my precious children were dead, it would be all due to my selfishness in wanting to keep them with me. With a sudden sickening whooshing sound and a gush of dust, the wall at the far end of the cellar collapsed.

The dust was suffocating and I could feel the rough grains of concrete powder clogging the back of my throat and up my nose. I choked, spluttered and spat, desperately trying to clear my airways and breathe properly. After what seemed an agonisingly long time I began to take easier breaths and my panic began to subside. Joyce was lying down next to me. I pulled my head scarf off and began to try and clear her nostrils and mouth. After a few seconds she spluttered back to life and the two of us clung onto each other and prayed we would live though this.

I lost sight of Susan and must have dozed off for a while. When I awoke I was relieved that I could definitely hear the sounds of voices outside the cellar. Small shafts of natural light were filtering through and I hoped rescue was imminent. There were men's voices nearby shouting instructions and the noise of them brought me comfort, they sounded as though they knew what they were doing. I began to feel less afraid.

About a half hour later a man was lowered through a small hole on a rope. He brought with him a sense of elation that surged through my body. It now seemed certain that we would we would all get out alive and my relief was palpable. I said thank you to God for sparing me and was happy this grubby cellar would not be my final resting place.

Our rescuer informed us that we would all get out but it may take a while. He explained that the rescue party had attempted to dig a bigger hole but that had caused the collapse of the wall earlier on. I realised this must have triggered the cloud of dust that almost choked us all. He went onto say they were unable to make the hole he had come down any bigger so the only way was to haul us up one by one.

I admired the bravery of the elderly man who had been lowered down to reassure us. It must have taken a lot of guts to come down into a semi-collapsed room. I sighed; I was feeling a little weary and knew I would have to hold on until it was my turn. It was nerve wracking as I sat and waited patiently clasping Joyce's hand as much for my comfort as hers.

I waited uncomplainingly, but with some agitation, as the badly injured were pulled out first. Next to be freed were the walking wounded then the women. Despite my injury, I waited with Joyce, who had no physical wounds, because her terror was so acute and I couldn't leave her alone in such a state. At long last, the rescuer summoned Joyce to come forward, I watched as they tied rope around her waist. The poor girl looked absolutely petrified and her tears fell leaving long, clean rivulets on her dirty face.

I kept looking at her and smiling, hoping that I would be offering a little bit of comfort. My heart almost stopped when Joyce was almost halfway towards freedom. One of the rescuers, above ground, must have stumbled and fallen because she began to fall at an alarming speed back towards the cellar floor again. Her screams filled the room then came to an abrupt stop. She was winded and left dangling in mid-air, flaying her arms legs about as she tried to gain control.

I shouted at her to calm down and my voice seemed to penetrate through her panic and she became still. She was then pulled up again and I watched her disappear up through the small hole. Next was my turn. I felt like I should give my place to a more deserving person but the urge to get out of this would-be tomb was overwhelming. I was truly relieved to feel the rope being tied around my middle and see my feet being lifted off the ground.

The rope dug into my skin through my overall and I constantly had to catch my breath on the way up. I tried to help by grasping the rope to take some of the pressure off my stomach but this didn't help and by the time I was trying to think of another method to ease my discomfort, I was being pulled out of the ragged hole by a handful of dust covered men.

It was now early but still quite light. I drew in deeply my first lungful of clean air and this made me cough violently. Thirstily, I drank the cup of water an ARP warden pushed into my hand. I was then led to a nearby tent where my head wound was stitched and I was checked for any other injuries. I will never forget the joy of breathing unhindered after hours trapped in a dust-filled room. Once I had been assessed, I was given a blanket and a cup of tea. I was told to try and make my way home when I was ready. I enquired about the children in the nursery but no one could give me any answers.

I left the first aid tent as soon as I was allowed because I didn't want to get in the way of the people who still needed treatment. I walked out into the evening air, unsure what to do and then I saw her. Edna was stood behind a hastily erected cordon. She was holding Hester's hand and carrying Daisy. The elation I felt at the moment will never ever leave me. It felt, all at once, as though the world was full of birdsong and joyous harmony. My children were alive and that was all that mattered to me at that precise moment.

I hobbled over to Edna with tears of happiness in my eyes. Edna was a little tearful too; she explained she had been waiting for the last six hours to hear if I was alive or dead. She had being going to and fro her home to feed her family and do chores then sporadically came back to the factory any time she could. Edna had not been working that day, luckily, so she had not been in the cellar when the enemy plane had crashed into the factory. As we headed home I held Daisy close and clung onto Hester's tiny hand.

Edna told me that forty five people had been killed when a German Fokker had landed on the top of the factory. The nursery and workplace were flattened but the two metal Anderson shelters had protected the children and staff. She explained that it would take a few days to repair the factory in order to get it back to aiding the war effort. I made up my mind, there and then, to use those days off to take Hester and Daisy to Lucy in Ireland. It would break my heart in two but it was my duty to keep my daughters safe and I could no longer do that while they remained in Bristol.

16

MICHAEL ROSENTHAL

We were surprised to discover that here was a cinema in the nearby town to where we were based. I and my comrades often went to watch a film on our evenings off. The movies we watched were subtitled but most of what we viewed was very entertaining. The plushness of the place was a glaring contrast to our living conditions.

Even though where we were stationed was little more than a large hovel of sheds, I tried to make the best of it. I told myself to be happy that, for the moment, all was peaceful where I was posted and that should be enough. Some poor chaps were in violent war zones where every day could be their last so I shouldn't complain about a little discomfort in my living conditions.

It was also exciting to go exploring around the shopping districts in this strange and exotic country. I knew that if it wasn't for the war I would very likely not have experienced the climate and culture of a foreign country. All in all, my lot was not a bad one and I had made, what I knew, would lifelong friends amongst my fellow soldiers.

We had been at the barracks for three days when, during the morning roll call, we were told pack up our belongings as we were heading for Singapore. I looked forward to visiting a different country and quickly obeyed my orders. Less than half an hour later, we all queued somewhat despondently to get back into the dreaded lorry crates. The journey here had been horrendous and it was lot shorter than the one we were now embarking upon and I did not relish the hours ahead.

I think we all felt the same and were dreading the weeks of travelling that we would have to do to reach our eventual destination. Thankfully we made several stops during the journey. We camped at several places along the way, including Kunming and Hanoi.

We travelled through China and Hong Kong and I longed to stop and take a look around but stops were brief and hurried. Finally and with great relief we reached our destination. I barely had time to look at my new surroundings before we were ordered out of our transport and directed towards a concrete walkway that would lead us directly into Singapore.

I was pleasantly surprised at the way the people on this island were going about their business, as usual, when I'd heard so many rumours that invasion and war was imminent. It was a beautiful country. The houses or pagoda's as they were known were all built on sticks so the onslaught of water wouldn't be able to reach them in the rainy season. The city was full of shops, cinemas and even an amusement park. I was happy to see that this camp was a vast improvement to our previous one.

There was plenty of water and clean lavatories which automatically meant better hygiene and less decease. Our sleeping quarters were indoors so there was less need of the mosquito net although I thought I'd hold onto mine case I had a need for it at some point. Once we had settled into our new 'home' we found out that the 'NAFFI' was the place to be and this was where most of us headed to in our free time.

Beer was served and there was record player in the corner with a large supply of records. There was a lot of camaraderie between myself and the other men. We talked about how lucky we were to be stationed in such a wonderful place when other British fighters had suffered the defeat at Dunkirk and how all the English cities were being relentlessly bombed night after night. We concluded that, happily, we were probably in one of the safest places on earth at this moment in time.

I had been at the camp for just over three weeks when a mail bag was dropped in. I ran, excitedly over to it, eager to hear from my loved ones. It took a long time to sort the mail but finally, I was handed five letters, two from Lucy, one from Len, one from Violet and the other was from Gerta. I raced back to my billet to read them in private. I ripped open the envelope in eager anticipation and began to read my news from homeland.

Scanning through them instantly took my mind back to the luscious emerald fields of Ireland and I longed to be back among the people I loved. All I could do was wait and hope it wouldn't be long before we were all reunited once more. I felt very close to my family when I was holding the letters that they had once held.

Gerta wrote asking how I was and told me to keep myself warm and look after myself. Violet and Lens letters were in the same vein but they also wrote and told me what was happening in their own lives. We were all eager for the war to be over so we could resume normal family life once more. Most of what Len wrote was censored but I got the gist of his letter and under-stood why the government had blacked out where he actually was in the world. I knew the letter could easily have got into enemy hands and put Len and his crew mates in danger if they knew of his whereabouts.

Lucy wrote to tell me that she had managed buy a wonderful new coat made of lamb's wool which was so soft to touch she kept rubbing her hand up and down it. She also told me that a bird with odd colouring had landed on the kitchen window sill and it reminded her of me. I laughed and took this as a compliment and was ultimately glad that the rest of my family was still safe and alive.

We had been in Singapore for four weeks when a small battalion of men, including myself, were ordered across the causeway and into the dense forest of Southern Malaya. Our mission was to collect a large amount of ammunition that had been delivered by ship. We were all in a jovial mood and looking forward to doing something different from our normal, and a little mundane, daily activity. Life in the armed forces was certainly not what I expected it to be, I had yet to face any combat and was quite happy about that.

As we made our way toward the think blanket of trees, Benjy Dawson, a man who had become a close friend of mine stopped and shushed us all. Above us, high in the branches was a small black bird. Dawson told us that it was a '*Javan Mynah*' and that originally, it had been breed as a pet bird but now lived in the wild. We all watched as its head jerked from side to side then it let out a loud squawk and flew out of sight. I thought the little creature was beautiful with its black, glossy feathers looking as though they had been polished to perfection.

Benjy had told us all how he enjoyed birdwatching before the war and how he found the hobby calming and interesting,

I nodded in agreement and told him how I was waiting to indulge in the same hobby as soon as the war was over. We turned to make our way towards the imported ammunition store and that was when the noise of a shot rang out. I turned, as if in slow motion, towards Benjy. He stood for a moment then slid to the ground. I dropped my gun and rushed towards him. He was lying on his back, staring at nothing. I shook him and his head lolled to the side and I realised the back half of his skull was missing.

I sat in a kind of limbo, shocked to the core, looking down at the man who had been alive and well a second ago, what had happened? I couldn't think who would have shot kind and gentle Benjy, a man who'd give you his last penny if you needed it more than him. Then another shot rang out and Gerald 'Smithy' Smith fell to the ground groaning and holding his shoulder.

I looked ahead and saw the terrifying figure of a Japanese Soldier racing towards me; his face, it seemed to me represented a pure personification of evil. I crouched unmoving, as though I was frozen in time as I heard the man screeching out words I didn't understand. His eyes were as black as coal and he wore terrifying camouflage make up that made his appearance even more devil-like. His nostrils were wide and flaring as he held up his weapon and aimed at my head.

I felt as if I was moving in slow motion as I dived to the ground and retrieved my discarded weapon. Without hesitation, I rolled onto my back and took aim. I shot the man directly between the eyes. He fell like a stone and remained motionless on the ground. I dropped my gun quickly, as though it was suddenly burning hot, unable to believe that I had actually shot another human being. As I stood, swallowing deeply with disgust at what I had done, another Japanese soldier appeared a small distance away.

I drew myself to my full height and tried but failed retrieve my weapon once from the ground once more. As I stood, I saw a picture reel of my life fly through my mind as though the whole of my existence was being fast forwarded. Without further hesitation I hurled myself at the enemy and sent him sprawling to the ground, knocking his gun from hand.

We rolled around, locked in mortal combat. Neither of our weapons was near enough for us to use. I fought desperately but I could feel myself weakening as I was subjected to punch after punch.

I began feeling around with my hand in an effort to find my gun but instead I felt the jagged sharpness of a large rock and grasped it in my hand. I gripped it tightly then smashed it into the side of my assailant's head. I likened the sound to that of an egg cracking. Again and again, I smashed it into his head until there was nothing solid to hit, just a mess of pulp and blood. Eventually a sound filtered through and into my brain and finally I heard someone yelling:

'He's dead mate, leave it!' over and over again but it was not until the rock was physically wrenched from my hand that I stopped my assault.

Johnson, another of the small party had jumped out from behind the tree he had been hiding behind. He congratulated me hurriedly and helped to my feet. I briefly looked at what was left of the skull of the man I had fought and vomited. Johnson patted my shoulder. My sergeant also then appeared as if out of thin air and quickly shouted, ordering all of us to get back to base on the double. His voice broke me out of my state of shock and I immediately sprang into action.

I retrieved my rifle then Johnson and I hoisted Smithy to his feet between the two of us and began following the rest of the party as we raced back. The sergeant and two other men were constantly on alert, looking for any other hidden enemy. It appeared to me that our assailants may have been a couple of lone wolves who just happened to stumble upon us, until we were just yards from the safety of the camp.

I dragged Smithy, by his uninjured shoulder to safety behind a large tree as more shots started to ring out. They flew past my head, alarmingly close and I raised my weapon ready to shoot. I could hardly believe my bad luck when my weapon jammed and refused to discharge any bullets. I peered from my hiding place and noticed Smithy's weapon a few yards from the tree, he must have dropped it as we fled.

The rest of the men had retreated behind various hiding places and began firing back in the general direction of the foe. Between a break in the shooting I hurled myself to the ground and crawled on my belly towards Smithy's gun then grasped hold of it. I slithered back behind the tree but not before I felt a burning sensation in my back. I ignored the pain as it seemed irrelevant in the situation we now found ourselves in. It felt ironic that just a short time ago I had been thinking how lucky I was that I had never had to face any armed conflict.

I cranked Smithy's weapon and began to fire at the enemy. I shot at anything that moved and was happy to see two more of the Japs fall to the ground. I soon realised we were heavily outnumbered by the amount of shots being fired at us. Without warning, a massive explosion about two miles from where were literally shook the ground. We used this diversion to make our escape from the ambush we found ourselves in. Johnson and I continued to drag the injured Smithy back with us, running as fast as we could with our fallen comrade.

Shots rang past my ears, so close that I thought the noise would make my head explode. Once we were clear of the jungle we could see the causeway in plain view. I was half relieved and half frightened because now we no longer had the cover of the trees and foliage to shield us from the barrage of bullets. If the Japanese caught up with us, we would be sitting ducks.

As I raced along the concrete pathway, I could see English Soldiers back at our base shooting at the enemy and I began to feel a smidgeon of hope that we might actually make it back to the barracks alive. It felt like I'd been running for days and the added weight of my wounded buddy was being to exhaust me. The barrack gates were yanked open as we approached and then we were safely inside. I staggered and fell to the ground. My lungs were burning and my back was killing me. I could feel wetness on the back of my shirt and when I put my hand on the spot, I found it covered in blood.

I knew it couldn't be a serious wound; otherwise I would not have been able to flee, at such sped, from the attack. This, however, did not stop it being extremely painful. I felt weak and sick but need to stir myself and join the other lads who were defending the island. I tried to stand but staggered then collapsed into blackness. I woke sometime later in the hospital quarters. The nurse told me that I had a nasty flesh wound to my lower back but other than that I was fine.

I asked her about Smithy, she held my hand and told me she was sorry but that he didn't make it and was probably dead before we got back. I found it tremendously hard to make sense of losing two very close friends in the same amount of hours. It didn't seem real that one minute we were discussing a species of bird then were under attack. I was swiftly discharged from the hospital tent and allowed back to my billet. I walked into the building to find a sombre union of men and listened in shock to the news they relayed to me.

The Japanese had already invaded Malaya and had their sights set on Singapore. Of the eight men who were sent out to get the ammunition, only three returned and I was one of the lucky ones, or so I thought at the time. The loud explosion we had heard mid battle was the sound of the British army destroying the bombs we had been sent to retrieve to ensure the enemy didn't get their hands on them. I now knew that Britain was on the run and I was terrified. My peaceful existence had been well and truly shattered and I had no idea what would happen next.

A picture of Lucy came into my mind and I longed to hold her, if only for a second. I was sure her presence would be a salve on my frightened mind. I wanted to touch her soft, lamb's wool coat and bury my head in her hair. I didn't know then that a totally different man to the one I was now would return home to Lucy. This new creature I became would cause her more hurt than she would ever deserve. If I had known this I would not have returned home. I had no inkling that the lifelong nightmare would haunt me to my death.

17

February 14 1942
LEONARD ROSENTHAL

I had always adored being at sea. I loved the bobbing sensation under my feet made by the ebb and flow of the tide. The salty air always revived my senses and life on board a ship was what I thought I had been born for. That though, was only in peacetimes, now, however, it was different and our role in this war was an important one. We had the unenviable task of providing the British population with food and other necessities and ours was a dangerous position to be in.

Since the Teakwood had become the first British boat to be attacked, all merchant navy ships now travelled the seas surrounded by armed vessels as we toured around the world to bring supplies to England and any other allies that might need it. I could not let my mind dwell on the enemy submarines that lurked way below the surface waiting to blow us up at any given opportunity. Holding on to these thoughts would drive me mad so I pushed them out of my head.

I worried constantly about Violet, Hester and Daisy because I knew Bristol was suffering more than its fair share of air raids. I and the rest of the crew, when we weren't on duty, would huddle around the Bakelite radio in our cabin, whenever we could, to try and listen to what was happening to our loved ones. London was also having a terrible time of it and we all felt helpless, adrift in the middle of the ocean. I couldn't work out if being aware of what was happening back home was a good or a bad thing.

A few days later after I had been working a nightshift I was sound asleep in my hammock in the middle of the day when a torpedo hit. In my semi-sleep I thought I felt the ship list but, at the same time, I thought it was only in my dreams. It wasn't until the warning hooter rang out that I came to my senses and hastily rubbed the sleep from my eyes. I rolled off my hammock and quickly shook myself awake.

Pulling on my bell bottom trousers and buckling my belt as I went I raced up to the top deck. It was quite calm but there was a group of men at the far end straining to see over the side of the ship. I joined them and craned my neck to see what was happening. I could see a jagged hole in the side of the ship which wasn't a particularly big one but it seemed to be taking in a lot of water. There was fierce fighting going on between the British army and our German attackers all around us.

There were also cat fights going on in the sky above us and both enemy and friendly fire were exploding above us as the Royal air force fought to protect the fleet. I watched and saw planes literally drop out of the sky then fall into the ocean. I couldn't help but thinks what a criminal waste of human life was happening all around me. Innocent men were dying and for what? There would be no countries left, on either side, if the continual bombing raids did not end.

By the time Hitler had finished blowing up most of England there would be nothing left for him to conquer. The word, through the local grapevine, was that he had never dropped a bomb on the city of Blackpool because this is where he wanted to live once he had invaded our clean and pleasant land. I knew, for sure, that the man was a deranged monster and knew in my heart that he had to be stopped, but at what cost to mankind?

My thoughts began to depress me so I turned my mind to more urgent practicalities and headed down below. I was pretty sure that the ship was not going sink because it seemed to have steadied itself and remained afloat. I returned to my cabin and dressed myself fully now I knew that I was not in imminent danger. I then went further below deck to the point where the vessel had been hit.

Water was pouring in at an alarming rate. Over fifty men were chucking the seawater out of the hole with any implement close to hand while another twenty clambered outside in an effort to repair the gaping gap in the boat. I grabbed a bucket and joined my fellow men. Frantically, we tried to expel as much water as we could. It was hellish, unending job but we battled on.

The water in the ship was icy cold and I stood knee deep in it for what felt like a long lifetime. It was so chilly, it made my legs ache and my fingers go numb. I didn't give in to my discomfort, though, and pressed on with the task of saving the ship. We were joined by more men who began to work as feverishly as we were. Now I was sweating form every pore as the job before me became ever more daunting as more water appeared to pour into the vessel.

Suddenly and abruptly the inflow of water ceased. To mine and the rest of the crew's enormous relief, we realised that while we were trying to empty out the ship, the engineers had been on the other side trying to close the gaping hole and thank God, they had succeeded. The fissure was temporarily but adequately plugged and the water had stopped coming in. I cheered loudly as did the rest of my shipmates.

Once I knew the ship was safe, I staggered back to my bed feeling utterly exhausted and chilled to the bone. Sleep, however, would not come and I swung, listlessly, on my hammock as the ship limped onwards. A few days later the vessel finally reached its eventual destination in Russia and the wretched craft looked like a pathetic sight. The vessel was anchored up. We were told we would have to remain ashore while the ship was being repaired, a small price to pay for being alive. However, I was not happy ashore in this strange and cold place.

I constantly pondered if the Russians were grateful to us for travelling thousands of miles to bring those much needed supplies of food, medicines and weapons. The people seemed an odd and miserable bunch of people that fitted in with their dull, grey surroundings. They did not speak as we unloaded our cargo in the freezing conditions but just eyed us with a mixture of contempt and distrust. I had no idea why because we were fighting on the same side.

I was always glad when we were sailing out of the grey port and heading back into the open sea. Now, however, we were to remain here until the ship was made seaworthy enough to get us home. I had never before experienced such bone-chilling coldness as I did when sailing on the Russian convoys. The iciness seemed to penetrate through to my bare skin no matter how many layers I wore. I wondered if the locals ever felt warm. They certainly didn't have sunny personalities.

I couldn't understand how humanity survived in such extreme conditions but I supposed if that was all a person was used to, they wouldn't know any other way of life. I went below deck to collect what items I would need for our short stay in the country and marched reluctantly with the rest of the crew to the village hall which would be our billet for as long as we stayed here. The hall was freezing cold even though we were all kitted out with great coats, thermal underwear and anything else that might keep us warm.

A communal cheer sounded throughout the whole building when two Russian peasants carrying a large paraffin heater between them entered. Maybe they were grateful to us after all. We all clambered around when it was eventually lit and finally it began to throw out an unexpected amount of warmth and we were able to remove our outer wear. Later on, when the evening was closing in, some sullen looking ladies appeared and began to distribute chunks of bread and cheese. This was a welcome feast to add to our meagre diet and the cheese melted in my mouth.

A tea urn was provided and as the cooks began to brew up, the smell of the drink once again reminded me of home and Violet. I imagined her in our little kitchen waiting for the kettle to screech, once the water had reached boiling point, then pouring the hot water over the loose tea. I longed to be at home with her instead of here, in this frozen, soulless place.

Something that did bring a smile to all our faces arrived later that evening. Small bottles of vodka were handed to those in charge and distributed to us men. I hadn't tried vodka before. I found it pretty tasteless but loved the sensation of warmth it gave me as it trickled down the back of my throat. It also helped me to sleep on the hard floor and I dreamt that I was home once again in the heart of my little family.

18

February 15 1942
MICHAEL ROSENTHAL

The fall of Singapore was swift and unexpected. Oddly enough, just an hour before the invasion, the inhabitants of the country were going about their business as though nothing unusual was happening. The fierce fighting must have alerted them to something, yet still they carried on with their daily chores. The Japanese enemy marched into our camp like a swarm of flies. I admit I was absolutely terrified and surrendered my weapon to them immediately and without question.

I had read many stories about the enemy and knew that a Japanese warrior would rather kill himself than yield. I preferred to stay alive; I wanted to see my Lucy again and smell the fresh green moss that clung onto the rocks that were dotted along the Irish hillside. I had also heard about Japanese kamikaze pilots who went on suicide missions with the intent of taking as many innocents with them. In my mind, this made them seem like unhinged barbarians and their very presence made the hairs at the back of my neck stand on end.

All these things I knew about the enemy convinced me to do exactly what I was told to do. These men sent a shiver down my spine. Their small, narrow eyes seemed almost black and they obviously enjoyed putting the fear of God into anyone who disobeyed their orders. My squadron leader was beaten with the butt of his own gun when a pistol, he had hidden down the back of the waist band of his trousers, was discovered by the Japanese invaders. I turned away as I heard his cheekbone crack, I couldn't bear to look. I felt like a miserable coward.

I made up my mind, there and then to be totally compliant to the enemy. At the time I badly wanted to stay alive and would have done anything to achieve this aim. After much shouting and screaming, in a language we didn't understand, we were all shoved or manhandled outside onto the parade ground. We were told by a particularly disagreeable looking Jap, in stilted English, that we were going to Burma as prisoners of war. I wondered what mode of transport we were going to use for the long journey back to Burma. The lorry crates we arrived in didn't seem such a bad idea now.

The night before we were due to leave I looked out into the night sky and wondered what was to become of us all. In my mind, all though the enemy seemed a demonic, distant race they must need us for some purpose, otherwise why would they take the trouble of making us return to Burma. This thought comforted me somewhat and I snuggled further down into my camp bed and drew my one solitary blanket up to my neck.

We were woken the next morning, by the sounds of fierce shouting and gun shots. I threw myself out of bed and dragged on my uniform in record time. We were, once more, bustled outside where our captors informed us that we would be leaving the camp shorty. I managed to smuggle out a small penknife and my picture of Lucy in the pocket of my tunic without being spotted by the guards. I regarded Lucy as my good luck charm and until we were together again, I would have to make do with her photograph. A few minutes later, we were ordered to leave the camp immediately.

Pushing us roughly out of the exit with obvious and unconcealed contempt etched on the evil faces of our captors, we were shoved out of the gates to the compound. Without realising, I stared at one of the Japanese soldiers, he looked devoid of all emotion, almost as if they were empty inside and when he saw me looking at him he raced over and smashed my brow with the butt of his gun. Blood trickled down my face and into my eyes. From that day onwards I kept my eyes to the ground whenever the enemy were nearby.

As I held my battered face I felt an overwhelming, almost compelling urge to close my eyes and be magically transported back to the lush green countryside of Ireland and to feel Lucy's soft hand in mine. Sadly, I knew all too well, that this was an impossible dream. I stood amongst my fellow detainees until we were given the order to move once more and prayed that God would not forget us like, it seemed, the rest of the world had.

I took one last look back as were frog-marched back along the concrete causeway we had arrived on. At first, I tried to walk upright and with pride but as the days passed by, my body began to stoop with exhaustion, lack of adequate food and water and the relentless, seemingly unending, journey.

The only food we were given, along the way, was small amounts of rice and a watery fish stew that tasted vile but I ate it anyway. The water we drank was discoloured and tasted of tin. I felt weak and weary as did my fellow men but we did not succumb to our exhaustion and continued to march along as we were ordered to.

The terms of the Geneva Convention dictated that any prisoners of war should be treated humanely by their captors. Also, it advised that anyone who became ill should be adequately treated by doctors and given medicine if needed. The convention was also meant to ensure that all the POWs were housed in civilized conditions.

I was pretty sure that the enemy had not signed the agreement because they treated us no better than dogs. Any man who became unwell or tripped and fell was shot or stabbed then kicked into a ditch to be left to die at the mercy of any wild animals that stumbled upon them.

My whole body was continuously infused with fear and I was absolutely sure my captors could smell it. Sometimes I was sure I could feel their eyes boring into the back of my head. I knew there were many ways in which death could grasp me and I wanted to live. I made a decision to take note of any man who seemed unwell so I could keep as far away from that person as I could, wherever possible, so he would not pass whatever he was ailing from onto me.

I was downright determined to fight any off any of the many diseases that plagued us prisoners. I was also aware that if the journey continued for much longer, I knew the exhaustion and malnutrition I was plagued with would not unable me to physically battle them. I thought it would be easier to avoid sickness of any kind than attempt to fight it until we had reached our destination and hopefully got some rest and proper nutrition.

At that time, getting home was the most important thing to me. If I had known then how things were going to turn out I would have stayed in the jungle where I wouldn't be able to harm the people I loved. So I kept my head down and marched without complaint but as the days turned into weeks, I wondered if death would be a heavenly release.

My body was becoming weaker and my mind began to wander. Sometimes, I closed my eyes and imagined I was back home in Ireland. Imagining myself back on British soil helped me to endure the inhuman conditions I found myself in.

Finally our long march took us to Sarawak, on the edge of the South China Sea. The ocean glistened and sparkled in the early afternoon sun and I longed to throw off my filthy uniform and dive in, I dared not. Docked and obviously waiting for our arrival was an ancient boat which I later found out was an old paddle steamer. The vessel looked as if it was about to sink at any moment and creaked and groaned in line with the ebb and flow of the tide.

The Japanese began screaming at us and pointing their bayonets in the direction of the rotting gangplank. I was jostled forward with the rest of the men and scrambled onto the perilous craft. We were all forced into a tiny hold. The size of the space was such that we were so cramped that we could only stand. Sweat from our bodies mingled together and we urinated where we stood. The air became acrid and humid and breathing became difficult. I was tall enough to be able to hold my head above some of the other men and gulp in some warm air.

I still found it hard to breathe, as did the rest of the prisoners. At first, the stronger ones in our party talked among ourselves; we did this to try and boost the morale of those who were failing and unwell. But, as the boat continued across the ocean, we all became silent, now too exhausted to buoy up the weak ones. I can only describe the horrendous journey as it was as though I was travelling in a coffin. The smells that emanated from our compacted bodies were overwhelming and sickening.

The poor unfortunate souls who met their demise on that unspeakable journey stood among us all until we arrived in Saigon. Their rotting corpses were attacked by no end of flies and other vermin but there was nothing we could do for the departed souls. Sometimes, throughout the journey I envied them because they no longer had to fight to survive. We were unable to help them or ourselves, they just festered where they stood. The appalling conditions merged with the sense of hopelessness in the fight for survival that haunted me until my dying day.

When the doors of the hold were finally opened and a warm breeze blow through, I held my mouth towards the air and tried to gulp it in an effort to rid my lungs of the rancidness that had been filling them. I was jostled along amongst the throng of stinking humanity until I was out of the stifling hold. The air caressed my face and it felt like a heavenly balm on my clammy skin. I stumbled across the gangplank and on to dry land.

My legs felt as though they would not be able to hold my weight. I had not moved them for so long, I felt as though I was on the verge of collapse, only fear kept me moving. Although the grass at our destination was spikily dry, it felt marvellous after the journey and I dug my toes in to the earth. Just a few minutes after we disembarked, the Japanese ushered us all onto a waiting truck. Because of the stinking smell of it inside I assumed it had originally been used for the transport of livestock. I guess that was what the Japanese now regarded us as, their very own cattle to use for work and to feed only when absolutely necessary.

The vehicle eventually stopped and we were all ordered out. I clambered down but was unable to stop myself from stumbling. A Japanese soldier bore down on me and rammed the butt of his gun into the back of my head. The blow made me feel nauseous and I could see little silver lights swimming around my eyes. I struggled to get to my feet, determined I would not become a useless body tossed into a ditch. I felt a pair of hands underneath my arm pits.

A man beside me hoisted me to me feet, I recognised him as Gerald Catchpole, known as Lanky because of his height and slimness. I mumbled my profuse thanks without either looking at him or acknowledging him and he nodded towards me very briefly. Neither of us wanted to bring the attention of the enemy to us. It was imperative that we melted into the crowd and made ourselves as invisible as we could.

We walked on until we finally arrived in a remote part of the jungle. I think the enemy liked to call it a 'camp' but I would describe it more as a dilapidated 'chanty village'. There were dozens of huts standing alongside of each other. Such was their ramshackle condition; I wondered how they remained standing.

It seemed to me that a strong breeze would blow them away. We were all pushed towards our allocated huts. I walked inside mine and the first thing I noticed were the large bugs crawling around the floors. Such was my diabolical condition the first thought that came into my head was that they'd make a tasty snack.

We were left to acclimatise ourselves for a short while and given water and a small portion of boiled rice. I looked about the place and was alarmed, but not really surprised, to see that there was no form of sanitation at all. This would mean that disease would be rife amongst the inmates. The lavatories were just long ditches where we all had to crouch to do our business and luxuries like toilet paper were unheard of. The only water supply came from a river running alongside the camp and was guarded heavily by our captors.

As we all stood to attention in our new home, a Japanese soldier explained in stilted English that we were to be prisoners here until the war ended. I listened as the man told us that there would be no escape. The surrounding jungle was dense and impassable he warned us. Any man caught in an escape attempt would be killed without mercy. As I listened, a sense of desperateness enveloped me so tightly I felt as though my chest wall would break.

As we were herded towards one of the bamboo huts, I took an inconspicuous look around. The Japanese soldier was right, the trees were so large and close together that it seemed like the slimmest creature wouldn't be able to fit between them. The clearing that we would now be residing in had obviously been purposely made for our arrival. I took the threadbare blanket I was allocated and claimed a place in the corner of the hut which we had been shown into earlier.

Although the billet was filthy, it was much better than being in the cramped, asphyxiating steamer hold or the stinking livestock truck. A short time later, probably less than ten minutes after we had eaten our meagre food ration, we were shepherded back out of the hut. I listened as we were all told that we would be building a railway that would run through the length of Burma. Later, I discovered it would be known as the Death railway due to the amount of men that would die erecting it.

The words that the Japanese Commandant screeched, as I stood to attention on the makeshift parade ground never left me, he said:

'You are remnants of a decadent white race and fragments of a rabble army. The railway will be built, even if we have to use your bodies as railway sleepers'

The nightmarish ordeal commenced. Day after day I worked in the burning sun. I felt like my back would snap underneath the pressure and that the heat was sucking all the strength from my body. Sometimes we worked in mud, so thick and deep, it reached our thighs. It was impregnated with leeches that clung onto our skin, burning our limbs as they clamped their bloodthirsty mouths on to us. They left scars that remained on my body until the day I died.

Bugs and pests also resided in the filthy mud and would bite and sting our malnourished bodies at every given opportunity. It felt to me that not only was the enemy hell bent on killing us, nature also wanted to give them a hand. Such were the inhuman conditions of our encampment; more and more men began to fall ill with dysentery and typhoid. There were no adequate medical supplies to treat the dreadfully ill British soldiers and a great many did indeed end up as railway sleepers as our Japanese captor had informed us they would.

I later learnt that for each of its two hundred and fifty eight miles linking Burma to Thailand, three hundred and ninety three prisoners of war and slave labourers had died from starvation, malnutrition and brutal treatment at the hands of the enemy. The allied death toll would be twelve thousand. The longer I remained in captivity, the weaker my body became and the flame of resolve the urged me to live began to flicker.

The heat in Burma was like nothing I had ever suffered, it was so ferocious it seemed to devour my body and sap any modicum of strength I fought to retain. Such was the harshness of my imprisonment I was now severely malnourished and both my legs were covered with weeping, festering sores that my weak, tortured body could not find the power to heal.

Despite this, I spent every agonising daylight hour, each day, working towards building a railway in the scorching sun with hundreds of other prisoners of war. I still could not comprehend how, our captors, the Japanese army, were so merciless and devoid of natural care that they would kill a prisoner if they so much as caught their eye. These people had to be otherworldly to treat a fellow man in such a despicable way. It seemed to me that they could not be part of the human race but some sort of alien creature that was hell bent on working us to death.

Because of this constant threat, I kept my eyes to the ground at all times and avoided any direct contact with the enemy. Eye contact was frowned upon; we were considered too lowly a creature to look the enemy in the face. My unrelenting fear was that another violent beating would certainly destroy my emaciated body and I would never see my beloved Lucy again.

Throughout the long, relentless days, with hunger forever clawing at my stomach and the never ending thirst for a small drink of water, I sometimes feared I would be driven insane with the aching longing for basic human necessities. I wanted to howl like a werewolf so the world would know about my suffering. I wondered if there was a God and, if so, what his plans were for me. I wondered if I'd done something terribly bad in a previous life to have been dealt so many heavy blows in this one.

I always hoped that the nights would help me escape from the blistering heat but, in reality, they were so cold my wasted, gaunt body could not warm itself. We all slept as closely as we could to each other to try and glean some human warmth from the next man's body. I felt no shame in embracing the man who lay beside me, if it helped me to survive. Uncontrollable, quaking bouts of shivering interrupted what sleep I could find. The situation was becoming intolerable for even the hardiest soul.

The hellish conditions were always worse when I first woke to another gruelling day. It seemed to me as though the hours of darkness had made me forget my predicament, with each new morning the torment began anew. Time stretched endlessly in front of me as another exhausting day dawned and I stumbled towards my work station.

I had been at the camp for barely a month but it seemed like much longer. On this particular occasion, I felt that I had barely slept the previous night. This was due to the severe coldness that seeped into every crevice of my body and my exhaustion was now hampering my movements. As I struggled to lift my pick axe in the air and drive it into the arid, rock-hard earth, a lapse in concentration made insane daggers of fear stab wildly at my trembling body. Without thinking, I had looked up and caught the eye one of my captors.

Instantly, I realised my fatal mistake and gazed manically down, almost immediately, at the ground as the Japanese guard walked towards me, gun raised and the bayonet gleaming in the light of the blinding sun. I tried to prepare myself for my inevitable death but, even feeling as bad as I did, I still didn't feel ready. Something inside me flared up at the injustice of what was to befall me.

In a flash, and with a speediness that surprised me, I hurled myself at the approaching enemy and threw him to the ground with as much power as I could muster, feverishly driven by the unerring need to stay alive. Caught unaware, my jailer fell to the ground and began to cry out as I pummelled at his yellow face, ruthlessly and without stopping until the man was still. I was panting wildly with the exertion of my attack but in that split second, I knew I had to escape this hellhole now, before it became my tomb.

I looked madly about and instantly spotted another advancing foe; the man's face was emotionless as he too lifted his weapon, aimed it at my chest and pulled the trigger. I closed my eyes in preparation for death. A millisecond later I heard the unmissable click of the gun jamming and miraculously, seeing my escape. I savagely launched myself at my adversary knocking him sideways, as I surprised him with my sudden attack.

I then straddled the man and set on him while he was still winded. I pulled my small penknife out of my trouser pocket at plunged it deep into his eyes over and over again. Blood squirted from each eye socket, drenching my face and hair, as the man screeched in pain. When he ceased to move I flung myself off the prostrate body and turned and raced towards the dense jungle as fast as my feeble legs would carry me.

I began to run, stumbling over tree roots that tore open the soles of my bare feet. Oblivious to the pain, I continued fleeing into the shelter of the jungle. I felt as though my chest would burst open with pain and I wondered if my withered body could take much more strain. After what seemed like hours but was probably minutes, I came across a cave, hidden partially by dead undergrowth, tree roots and dense foliage, here I hid. My body was quaking with terror as I stood as still as ice.

After a while I quietly squatted onto my knees, unable to hold my body up anymore. There I remained, rigid and unmoving with my ears acutely alert for any unwanted sound of my pursuers. I was almost afraid to breathe for fear of being found and could only wait and hope that I had out run the guards.

Chillingly, the noise of twig snapping alerted me to the fact that I was not alone. The fight or flight impulse washed over me and I chose the latter. I emerged from my hiding place and began to frenziedly lash out, flailing my arms around like a wild animal, fighting for my very survival.

19

February 16 1942
VIOLET ROSENTHAL

The powers that be did everything they could to get the factory back in working order as soon as they could. After a few days we were told that the building had suffered extensive damage and would be close for three weeks much to the work forces dismay. No job meant I wouldn't be earning a wage and I had become used to having my own money. However, it was important that the factory was safe to work in.

I took this opportunity to take my children to safety. I tried not to cry as I packed up their few possessions in a cardboard suitcase. I carefully folded Daisy's terry towelling nappies into tiny squares and placed the large safety pins and rubber pants on top of them. Her few romper suits had seen better days but there were very few places to buy new ones in Bristol.

Hester's clothes had also been repaired to death and I wished I could take my children to Lucy's home with a better garments. I managed to squeeze in Hester's crayons and colouring book but had to leave her tiny dolls pram under the stairs ready for her return. The only thing that kept me going through that awful time was knowing that they would both come back to me when the war was over and please God, let that be soon. I didn't want to be apart from my daughters a moment longer than I needed to be.

I walked to the station, with a heavy heart. It was slow going as Hester toddled beside me holding my hand and I carried the baby in my other arm. When we finally arrived at the station, both my arms were aching under the strain of everything I had been carrying. We were lucky we did not to have to wait too long for the train and we were some of the first people to board when it chugged into the station.

I gave Daisy a bottle as the train continued out of Bristol heading for Liverpool. When Daisy had finished her milk, I hastily replaced the bottle with a dummy. Now contented, Daisy remained quiet, thankfully. The train was packed and I was sure the rest of the passengers wouldn't want to be deafened by Daisy screaming for more milk.

Hester was as good as gold. She clung onto her toy rabbit as she stared out of the train window watching the world go by. I cuddled her close throughout much of the journey and she didn't seem to mind, as she usually did. I guessed maybe she had some childish intuition that we were going to be separated for a while. Other times when I had tried to smother her in an embrace, she would wriggle free and giggle then return to what she been doing before I accosted her.

As the train trundled through Liverpool I witnessed the destruction that a recent wave of enemy bombers had caused around the previous August. The city was under attack for three consecutive nights and there were also regular attacks over the rest of the year. At times only a few German aircrafts dropped their deadly cargo but other times as many as three hundred crafts filled the sky and were laden with doom and death. I imagined that many aircraft would have filled the heavens and hidden the clouds.

In September Walton Jail had been hit by a highly explosive device that had destroyed and entire wing and killed twenty two prisoners. I wondered if that was God's retribution but quickly dismissed that thought otherwise how could I explain the death of the innocents, I didn't really know. I decided it was better that the criminals got killed rather than someone who had committed no crime. They would have been imprisoned if they had not deserved it so I decided not to waste my sympathy on them.

The worst raid happened in November when an air raid shelter protecting over three hundred Liverpudlians took a direct hit. One hundred and sixty six people were killed and I shuddered as I tried to imagine the mind numbing fear they must have felt listening to the enemy aircraft flying above and then unleashing their deadly arsenal. I didn't want to imagine how terrified they must have been and said a silent prayer for the poor souls who perished.

It was heart breaking to witness the destruction of a once beautiful city. It struck me that if the Germans continued to bomb Liverpool there would be no city left for them to overcome. I could think of no realistic reason for war and destruction.

If only Winston Churchill could talk to Hitler face to face I was sure that our prime minister could talk some sense into the mad man. Or maybe, Adolf Hitler would simply 'lie' his way out of any debate like he had when our previous prime minister had visited the country before the outbreak of war. Chamberlain had been 'promised peace in our time' but it was just a ploy to give Germany more time to amass weapons armoury.

At least it also bought England some time to ready ourselves for invasion. The government used those months to build factories and erect barrage balloons. Football pitches were dug up and used to grow vegetables and Anderson shelters had been erected at the end of most streets. At least we were semi prepared when war was eventually announced.

I struggled out of at Lime street station with my daughters and their luggage. We then took a small bus ride to the port and the ferry that would take us across the Irish Sea and to safety. We boarded the ferry a short time later. I was feeling inexplicably nervous as I sat on a seat next to the window as the craft made its way across the ocean. The colour of the sea was as grey as Cornish granite though thankfully not too choppy for a chilly January day. I had never enjoyed being on a boat, I had never learned to swim so maybe that's what caused my anxiety anytime I found myself travelling across the unpredictable ocean.

I had not heard of the Germans bombing any of the ferries bound for Ireland as the country had elected to remain neutral during the war. I was not sure what else could have caused my unease but could only think that seeing the destruction of Liverpool had upset me more than I realised.

There was a little nagging voice in my head that told me the Germans might bomb the ferry for no reason but I tried to silence that voice as it was not helping to quell the nervousness I was feeling. I had not had the time to inform my sister-in-law about our arrival but I was sure she would look after Hester and daisy without any problems.

I was relieved and glad when we arrived at our destination and I felt the comfort of dry land underneath my feet. I took the luxury of a taxi once we had docked as both the girls and myself were very tired after our long journey. As the vehicle draw up outside Lucy little cottage, the door opened and she shot out, smiling widely when she saw who her visitors were. I guess she must have been looking out of her kitchen window and witnessed our arrival.

Lucy very kindly paid the cab fare then lifted Daisy out of my arms while I followed her into the house carrying Hester and our luggage. I put both the girls in Lucy's bed for a nap and they dropped off almost instantly and with little complaint. This was unusual as Daisy fought sleep at any given chance. Once I was sat in Lucy's lovely, cosy kitchen I felt my body relax. I hadn't realised how on edge I had been since the bombing of the factory. The journey had been very tiresome also and I was glad it was over.

The little kitchen was very comfortable. The warmth from the AGA oven against one of the walls was particularly inviting. Blue check curtains were hung at the tiny window above the well-scrubbed sink which matched the table cloth. The little room had a large, wooden dresser covering almost the whole length of one wall. It was littered with an array of matching cups, saucers and plates. Its shelves also held a photograph of Len and me on our wedding day and a picture of Michael looking very handsome in his army uniform:

'Would you like a piece of cake?' Lucy enquired as she walked over to a tin on the top of the dresser. I nodded and smiled as she cut me a hefty slice. I smiled again as I bit into it, when I had eaten every crumb I told Lucy:

'That was wonderful, I can't remember the last time I ate cake that was made from real eggs, not powdered ones and proper butter, and it literally melted in my mouth'

It was Lucy's turn to smile as she said:

'I don't know how you put up with all that rationing; I really enjoy my food and would be horrified if I couldn't get hold of it'

'Well, we're all in the same boat and if it helps us win the war then that's what we have to put up with,' I answered.

'Why don't you come and live in Ireland, its safe here and no one goes hungry?' Lucy asked

'What type of person would I be if I fled my city and left it at the mercy of the enemy? Where would the country be if everyone did that? No, Len and Michael are fighting for us so I'll continue to do my bit,' I declared.

Lucy looked a little ashamed and apologised and began to explain how much she missed Michael and how lonely she felt a lot of the time:

'At least you don't have to suffer horrors of air raids and being killed in your bed, you should be thankful,' I reprimanded.

Lucy looked distinctly uncomfortable and I softened towards the young girl, she had led a cossetted and comfortable before her fall from grace and was used to being spoiled:

'I know you have no idea how bad it is and that's why I'm here, Bristol is too dangerous for Hester and Daisy and I was hoping they could stay with you until the war is over, I'll send money for their keep and visit as often as I can,' I told her.

Lucy's smile lit up not only her whole face but the whole room as she described how she would be more than happy to take care of my children and thanked me for trusting her with my daughters. As I lay in the narrow single bed in Lucy's spare room, that night, mixed emotions kept me awake.

I was relieved that Hester and Daisy would be safe but miserable that I would be living apart from them. I gave myself a mental shaking and asked if Michael and Leonard would rather be at home and not fighting a vicious enemy and I instantly knew the answer. They had no choice and neither did I.

I fell into a deep sleep. At first it was untroubled due to my exhaustion but something was penetrating into my deep unconsciousness. I thought I could hear bombs falling and explosions but I knew that couldn't be possible because I was in Ireland, not the Mainland, and this country had not been attacked by the Germans. I tossed and turned in my slumber but did not fully awake and the noises eventually died down then diminished altogether. I decided that living through a war had made my subconscious think I was still in Bristol.

I woke the next morning feeling refreshed and ready to face whatever lay ahead of me. Sleep, I decided was a wonderful comforter and healer. I walked in the kitchen rubbing the sleep from eyes and found Lucy sitting chatting with her next door neighbour who was also Len and Michaels's cousin. The conversation seemed quite animated but stopped as soon as they realised I had entered the room:

'Were you talking about me?' I said laughingly, Lucy turned to me and said without preamble,

'Dublin was bombed last year but it's been safe ever since, we just wanted to let you know.'

Gerta stood rubbing Lucy's back as she spoke and I wondered if there was anywhere that was safe for my children. Gerta explained that it was probably a stray bomb from the Mainland and I chose to believe her. I couldn't risk taking my girls back to Bristol. I deemed that Donegal was the safer of the two places and hoped no more bombs would fall. Gerta broke the dreary silence that had fallen on us by informing me that she had a highchair and a cot in her cottage next door and if I gave her a hand Lucy could have them for Daisy.

I thanked Gerta but was puzzled as to why she would have these things as I knew she was childless and asked her about the children's furniture. Gerta explained that she had given birth to a little boy, many years ago, far too early and that he had been still born on the same day her husband was killed at work. She went onto say that she had never had the heart to get rid of them but realised that they were now needed.

I felt dreadfully sorry for the lovely lady and told her so. She waved a hand in front of her face and told me it was a long time ago but I swore I saw tears glistening in her eyes. I silently reminded myself that at least my separation from children was not permanent and I should be thankful that I had a family member to take care of them.

As the three of us carried the two items, the highchair and the unconstructed cot, over from next door I couldn't help thinking about the bombing raid over Ireland and prayed to God that it would be the first and last one on this little island. I longed for some sort of reassurance that Ireland would be safer than Britain. I knew that I had no choice but to leave Daisy and Hester here, though. Bristol was definitely the more dangerous of the two places.

The children finally awoke and I showed Lucy how to change Daisy's nappy and how to make her powdered milk. I then lifted Hester into the high chair and spooned some Luke-warm porridge into her mouth. I had to catch the early ferry back to the Mainland so there wasn't much time for goodbyes. I was only allocated two days off for my factory job and I couldn't afford to lose it by not turning up for work.

Gerta must have noticed my sadness because she walked over and held me tightly and promised, at the same time, that she would help Lucy in any way should could and take care of my girls as if they were her own. I hugged them both closely as I thanked them. The dreaded time arrived for me to leave and I felt that my heart would burst out of my chest such was the misery I felt leaving my two tiny daughters.

I kissed Daisy and cuddled Hester for as long as I could, I kept swallowing down that lump that caught in my throat. I didn't know how I would bare being apart from them; I likened it to losing a limb. That was the strength of the bond we all shared. I told Hester that she must be a good girl for aunty Lucy and Granny Gerta and that I would be back to visit very soon. I hugged Gerta and Lucy then I hurried from the little cottage and stumbled down the narrow lane virtually blinded my own crying.

I sat, with a very heavy heart, on the ferry back home and had to swallow back tears on many occasions. The further I travelled away from my beloved children the harder it became to keep my emotions at bay. The water was a lot rougher on the outward journey and by the time I reached Liverpool I was feeling extremely sick and glad to be home.

My arms felt empty, as did my core as I made the solitary journey back to Liverpool on the train. I was lulled to sleep to the rhythm of the rocking carriage taking me home to Bristol. I dreamed that I was taking Hester and Daisy to the park to feed the ducks and woke with wet eyes once more when I realised I was alone.

Walking into my empty home was very hard and, for one last time, I let my tears fall unhindered. After a short while I forced myself stop my self-pitying sobbing and put the kettle on the hob. Just as it screeched to a boiling point Edna appeared at the door. She put her arm around my shoulder and gave it a little squeeze, no words were needed, because Edna was a mother herself and knew how I felt.

She was however, delighted when I produced the real butter Lucy had given me. We buttered some toast and talked about mundane daily chores and starting work at the rebuilt factory the following day. Edna told me how astounded she was at the speed that the factory had been reconstructed. We both agreed that it was in the government's interest to get it back into production as soon as possible to keep armed forces supplied with whatever they needed. That night I prayed to God for the war to end soon so I could have my family back in one place once more.

20

March 9 1942
LEONARD ROSENTHAL

A kind of bleakness had inexplicably come over me over in the past few days. It seemed to stick to my skin like a damp coat that seemed to be getting heavier as the days went by. I thought that, soon, I would buckle under the weight of the imaginary garment. One bright burst of sunlight that delved into the miserable existence, I felt I was suffering from, was the arrival of a letter from Violet a few days previously.

She told me how Lucy had written to her to say that Hester and Daisy had settled well and seemed happy. She made sure Hester mentioned us in her prayers every evening and for this I was grateful. I couldn't bear it if my young daughters forgot I existed. The thought that I was missing my children growing up did little to improve my mood. It was highly likely that they wouldn't even recognise me by the time we met again and realising this dragged me further down into my imaginary mire.

It felt as though a dense smog was enveloping and smothering me and was penetrating deep into my brain; I wondered if this was what it felt like to go mad. I began to find it harder and harder to sleep even though I was dead tired after completing several twelve hour shifts. If I did manage to drop off at any point I would wake, a short time later, screaming and thinking that water was gushing into the ship, only to be shaken awake by my crew mates, Lofty or Jim, imploring me to stop shouting so they could get some sleep.

I felt terrible for waking them up but I was powerless to fight my invisible adversary. I understood we were at war and these were precarious times but at this particular moment I was not in any danger at all but my body felt as though it was standing in front of a runaway train. I trembled for no apparent reason and my mind was constantly troubled by what might happen to me.

I realised that I could not hide how I felt anymore because it was now affecting my fellow crew members and that would not do. Sleep was a valuable necessity that was needed by all to remain alert and do our jobs correctly.

I rose early the following morning, after yet another sleepless night. My anxiety was heightened by my exhaustion and I was dreading what I had to do. I hesitantly headed to the sick bay, wandering how I was going to explain to the medic about my invisible illness and worried that he would think I was a basket case. It took me a full minute of indecision before I timidly tapped on the door and then heard a confident voice call:

'Come in please'

Taking a deep breath I turned the plastic knob then pushed the door open. My palm was sweaty and my mouth felt as dry as sandpaper. The room smelled exactly like every other doctors surgery. It was as if the odour of disinfectant was trying to disguise the smells of a menagerie of bodily odours that threatened to penetrate through. The doctor indicated for me to sit down and when I had did this he asked me what my problem was. My first overwhelming instinct was leap up a run from the room but I knew I couldn't, I began:

'Um, it's a bit silly really, I've been trying to deal with it but now I'm keeping my mates awake with my shenanigans,' stuttering as I felt my face redden.

The doctor looked at me and introduced himself as Doctor Leo Cowling and told me to call him Leo. This immediately put me at ease little bit:

'Doctor, ah… Leo, I think I'm going mad,' Dr Cowling patted my shoulder and told me to continue:

'I can't seem to shake off an awful feeling of foreboding and doom, I'm shouting in my sleep like a bloody child and waking up my crew mates, every small unknown sound has me diving for cover and I can't stop thinking morbid thoughts,' I looked down and twiddled my thumbs together nervously:

'Tell me about your thoughts and dreams Leonard,' the doctor said quietly.

'Well, I lost my parents some years ago, I thought I had put it all behind me but now I keep seeing them in my visions and wandering if they want me to join them, I don't want to kill myself but I'm frightened something will make me try to, I keep thinking about my brother who's a prisoner of war in Burma.'

I sighed, the effort of explaining how I felt was both exhausting and humiliating:

'We've had no communication in months, my brother and I, my wife, Violet, she's evacuated our children my sister-in-law to Ireland but she's stayed in Bristol, images keep flickering in my mind of her dead or burning body because of all the bombing raids, sometimes I want to punch my head to get rid of the pictures but I'm not sure if that would help.'

To my utter shame I realised that tears were pouring down

my face, I now felt my shame was complete and I waited for the Doctor to burst into laughter and tell me to bloody well pull myself together and start acting like a man. Instead, he passed me a tissue:

'My dear fellow, don't think your alone with these thoughts, you have no idea how many chaps come to me with psychosomatic physical complaints,'

I felt better almost right away, firstly, because I was relieved that I was not the only one suffering from this disorder and secondly, it actually had a name, so I hoped that it was an illness that could be cured:

'So I'm not heading for the loony bin,' I asked.

'No Leonard, old chap you are not, you are suffering from combat exhaustion brought about by the constant fear of death and attack, and this can cause many psychological problems, including hypervigilance, paranoia, depression and loss of memory. Believe me, every man has his breaking point, I will prescribe you Sodium Pentothal which is a barbiturate which will calm your thoughts and generally slow down any irrational thinking, also I'll up your rum ration, take a couple of glugs before you go to sleep and that will cure your nightmares,'

To me, it seemed like a totally different man from the one that had walked into the room walked out. On entering the surgery I was sure that I was going insane and that my next port of call would be a padded cell and a strait jacket. Now I was just a regular guy with a recognised illness and medicine to cure me. The relief was instantaneous. I collected my medicine from the dispensary on board and also my extra rum ration. I felt relieved and glad that I had made myself visit the surgery.

Although, once the medication kicked in, I felt kind of groggy, like I was walking through a sea mist, my black thoughts soon disappeared and I floated through my shifts with a calm confidence. I realised now that my mind must have been overloaded and unable to cope but the medicine gave me a sort of padding around my brain that helped me to focus on the important job of winning the war.

I am pretty sure that medication allowed my battered senses to rest a little and protected me from everything that was happening around me. I wrote to Violet with renewed enthusiasm and could actually see the metaphorical light flickering at the end of a long, narrow tunnel. It was just a small illumination in a sea of blackness but it gave me hope that I would be back to normal self soon.

21

March 20 1942

MICHAEL ROSENTHAL

I was strengthened by fear because I knew that if I did not escape, I would be tortured and then beheaded. I had seen what happened to the poor wretches that were dragged back to camp after they had tried to escape into the jungle. They would arrive back at the camp with broken legs but would be forced to hobble on their useless, misshapen limbs while screaming in pain and begging for the mercy of death.

We would all be ordered to stop work to witness the punishment. The Japanese knew where to jab a bayonet into a man's body that would not instantly kill hill but would cause him excruciating pain. The would-be escapee would have his eyes gouged out by enemy fingers and his body beaten until he begged for mercy and screeched for his mother.

I would not allow that to happen to me, this was the decision I made as I fought my enemies. I refused to allow myself to become a sideshow to dampen the already defeated morale's of my fellow prisoners. I was no longer afraid of death, just the circumstances that lead to mine. I continued trying to fight but I finally recognised that, not only was I was hopelessly outnumbered, I was also weak and under nourished.

I felt that I must have been losing my mind, throughout the brawl, because I was pretty sure I could hear an English speaking voice but more astonishingly it sounded female. There was no way on earth there could be an English person out here in the Chinese Jungle, this was enemy territory. I fought valiantly to free myself but it was to no avail. What little strength I had left deserted me and I fell to the ground. To my utter horror I found myself overwhelmed by my assailants.

Every part of my body was being held down as though I was covered in mounds of heavy soil and I was unable to move any of my limbs. I wanted to scream and cry at the injustices of the world. I shouted for them to kill me now. A hand was clamped over my mouth then a dirty rag was shoved into it. My legs and hands were then bound tightly and a blindfold was pulled over my eyes. My tears soaked the cloth covering my eyes.

I can only describe my journey back to camp as one of hellish repulsion, knowing the horrors I faced on my return filled me with a white hot fear that burned through me as though someone was stabbing me with a red hot poker. I silently asked God why, sure He must realise that no human being should be allowed to feeling so utterly wretched and worthless.

I knew the fate that awaited me and longed for the comfort of my mother's arms around me, protecting me from what was to come. I wanted to fight some more but I knew it was utterly pointless. I let the tears continue to fall and be absorbed by the coarse material that covered them. I was spent and had nothing left to give. I readied myself for death.

I'm unsure if my mind was trying to separate me from my fate as I allowed it to transport me back to Ireland. I could almost smell the faint scent of my darling Lucy's Lily-of-Valley perfume. I imagined her soft hand wiping my tears away and felt her warm lips on mine. I prayed to God to keep her safe and well and to tell her that I would always love her. I hoped she would never have to hear what happened to me. Lucy was fragile girl and I knew she would not cope with life if she was aware of my immense suffering.

I allowed myself to be carried along by my captors. My final journey through the jungle ended more abruptly than I thought it would. I saw a shadow of darkness come over me, through the edges of my blindfold. I now knew that I was indoors and probably in a hut of some kind.

The fight had left me, there was now nothing I could do but wait for my violent death. I was, surprisingly, enveloped by an overwhelming emotion of relief that it was all about to be over. No more would I have to toil relentlessly and stare death in the face every second of the day. My body would become one of the sleepers on the Death railway, that was my fate and I accepted it.

I felt someone untying my blindfold from behind and pulling it off but the gag remained in my mouth making me feel nauseous. My eyes struggled to focus in the dim light. I blinked rapidly to try and clear away some of the fog that danced in front my face.

After a few minutes I could make out shapes. I thought I was in a tent of some kind but that was impossible, there were no tents where I was held. It reminded me of the camping trips I used to go on with my mother, father and Leonard. The smell was familiar. I felt confused because I knew this was not the prison camp.

I felt my arms and legs being untied and as my eyes grew more accustomed to my surroundings I could see exactly where I was. I opened my eyes wide and with open-mouthed incredulity, as I looked up into the face of a white female staring down at me. I thought I must be hallucinating as she gently took the gag from my mouth. She then dropped onto her knees and put her finger to her lips to indicate that I must be silent. Such was my absolute shock at seeing her, this gesture was totally unnecessary.

Another person entered and I was momentarily paralysed as I noticed the oriental features of my enemy. Only, on closer inspection, they were different than those of my captors. The person handed me a metal mug of water, I began to gulp it down but the English speaking women advised me to sip it slowly, I did. Once I had finished, she began to speak:

'My name is Tung-Mei, I am the daughter of a Chinese mother and an English father,'

She bent down and helped me into a sitting position then handed my empty mug to the other person of Eastern heritage then continued:

'I have lived in Singapore all my life and even when the Japanese threatened to invade, my father assured me that the British would not allow Singapore to fall, sadly he was wrong, when my country overrun by Japan, we just ran and kept running; we now fight for New China and will continue to do so until we are free,'

She then introduced me to her companion, his name was Zihao Son, Tung Mei carried on with what she was saying:

'My family fled to the West when the Japanese attacked Shanghai, it was not an act of war, it was murder, they dropped bombs on thousands of innocent civilians killing many and injuring thousands more. Millions of Chinese citizens relocated to the West to what we call the New China,'

Tung Mei stopped and took a breath as though she was trying to compose herself then he continued:

'I have chosen to stay behind and fight as have Zihao and many others. We are all mainly manual workers, particularly farmers but we have trained to become killers and we will not hesitate to execute any Japanese patrols that search for us. We will not allow them to go to the West and wage war on our new country,'

She placed her hand on my cheek and rubbed it softly. The touch of a female hand on my weather roughened made me want to sob once more. I wanted her to hold me close so I could rest my head on her chest and tell her everything that had happened to me. I did not. I simply put my own hand over hers and thanked her:

'Please rest, we will talk later, you are safe here.' She assured me.

Tung-Mei walked out of the canvas shelter followed by Zihao Son and I sat, unable to comprehend what had just happened to me. I shook my head, as if it would help to untangle my thinking. A very short while ago I had allowed myself to come to terms with my own impending demise, yet here I was, alive and seemingly safe. It was hard to take in and I wanted to cry like a baby but I fought to keep myself composed, I had been given a second chance of life and I silently thanked God.

22

March 25 1942
LEONARD

Now we were a long way from the iciness of the Russian landscape, the arctic chill had been replaced by a blanket of thick, grey fog. It hung around leaving me enveloped in a pall of greyness that seemed to being crushing my spirit even with the help of barbiturates. I could see nothing through the thick mist and every tiny sound made me alert to the enemy presence. I hated the way I was feeling and wanted to make it all go away, although the feeling was not as all-encompassing as it used to be, it was still lingering around me.

The unexpected squawk of a sea bird made me throw myself to the deck and quiver with fear and I covered my head with my hands, ready for imminent attack and inwardly reprimanding myself for my foolishness. The sound of sudden laughter or any unexplained noise still made me perspire inexplicably and my eyes would dart around looking for an invisible enemy. I had received a letter from Violet a few days earlier that truly warmed my heart. I read it over and over and it helped keep me sane.

She told me how she loved her job at the aeroplane factory and about the new friends she had made, Susan and Joyce. She told me how Lucy had written to tell her that the girls had settled in well and were '*as happy as Larry*'. She made sure that she talked about us constantly to Hester and little Daisy and for that I was grateful. As yet, little Daisy was far too young to be aware of my existence and, when the war was over, if I was lucky enough to survive, I would have to get to know both of my children again.

Before the onset of war, working for the merchant navy was a joyful mix of visiting foreign lands and excitedly exploring their new cultures and customs. The other crew members, on board, were my friends for life and we were as close as brothers. Now that the war had started it was very different, each trip we made was fraught with danger. There were now people aboard that I did not recognise but was quite sure they were high up in the ranks of the military and were doing specialised highly dangerous jobs.

I did, however become friendly with one of these guys. His name was Desmond Masters and he was one of the friendliest chaps I had ever met. He was also one of most of the most unassuming people and I knew that his job was highly dangerous. Rumour had it that he was often parachuted into enemy territory and spent weeks at a time there posing as one of the locals. During his spells abroad he would gather as much information on enemy whereabouts and plans as he could without rousing suspicion. I was in awe of him. His bravery humbled me and strangely, many years later, we would meet again.

I and my crew mates were constantly on edge, our eyes always on the lookout for the hidden foe. Even when we were sailing in neutral territory, so I couldn't imagine how Desmond Masters coped walking amongst the enemy on daily basis, I thought the man must have nerves of steel. The lessening of my anxious feelings occurred so slowly that I was almost unaware it was happening.

It seemed as though the tight knot that was lodged in the middle of my stomach began to loosen somewhat. It was though the medicine was working at taking the edge off my fraught nerves and I began to finally feel a little happier in myself. My overly morbid thoughts began to drift away.

I told myself it was completely natural to be frightened. When we could actually see the enemy it was bad enough. But the terror increased tenfold when we were alerted to the presence of a U-boat deep beneath the surface of the water, waiting to blow us all to smithereens. It was as though there was a deadly cancer lurking below waiting and biding its time before leaping up and massacring us all in one deadly blow. It was perfectly natural to worry when living with the constant threat of death.

I loved life on the sea from the very minute I joined up before the war started. Now it made me feel angry and helpless fighting a faceless rival that would happily kill working sailors who were merely doing their jobs. The senseless butchery sent blades of anger gushing through my body I longed for it to end. I wanted to punch my fist through my stomach and pull my ball of anxiety out.

Other times I wanted to put a bullet in my stomach to erase the constant sphere of dread that rested in the pit of my gut like a festering sore. Respite was coming but much too slowly for me, I knew I had to be patient and allow the medication to do its work.

I was mildly comforted by the fact that we were always escorted by naval warships but I was worriedly aware that if, we came under serious bombardment, there would not be enough air and sea power to defend our fleet. I tried not to think about it too much but it was always there, in the back of mind, the thought that there were people who would rather we didn't exist. It was alarming and upsetting and something I would never become accustomed to, no matter how long the war raged on.

I often thought about Violet and the children and constantly worried about their safety. I wished Violet could also stay Ireland with Lucy but I knew my wife well and realised she would feel it her duty to help with the war effort. I was very proud of her. But even imagining her beautiful face wouldn't drive the deep wretchedness that I often felt, away.

Often, I wondered, in my own mind, what was the point of life in general. If Hitler won the war and Germany invaded England, I couldn't stomach living under German rule. All my life, I had tried to look on the bright side but now there didn't seem to be one.

My nightly dreams were peppered with images of my dead parents and I frequently lay awake worrying about Michael and what was happening to him. As far as I know, no one had heard anything from him for months. My fellow crew advised that 'no news was good news' but I couldn't rid myself of the feeling that something horrific had befallen to him. He knew that we would all be worrying about so, if he could contact us, he would have done so what was preventing him? I hoped and prayed he was still alive.

I had been informed by telegram that he had been captured and was now a prisoner of war in Burma. Gossip filtered through that the Japanese captors were barbarians who did not adhere to the Geneva Convention and the thought that something terrible had happened to Michael haunted me day and night. I didn't think I could bear losing another family member. I felt that, as I was the elder brother, I should be protecting him but I was not.

I received letters from Lucy, his wife, which were always upbeat and positive but I didn't know if this was what she truly felt or whether she was merely trying to 'buoy me up'. Lucy was apt to bury her head in the sand and pretend that all in her garden was rosy rather than face up to harsh reality. Maybe she had the right idea, who knew? The turmoil in my mind was alien to me and I was at a loss at what to do to pull myself out of my black mood quicker.

My crew mates kept saying that the war would drag on for years and I was sure I couldn't survive in this perpetual state of fear and gloom for months let alone years. There were posters all over the ship telling us 'to keep calm and carry on' and other slogans trying to lift my flagging spirits but it didn't succeed, I don't think I had a' stiff upper lip' or a 'bulldog spirit'.

I could see no end in sight. I was missing my daughters growing up and family life seemed a distant dream. Tonight, I was on the lookout duty and, thankfully, it was quiet and calm. The stars looked like tiny silver lights sparkling in the dark sky and illuminating the inky black sea. I wondered if Violet was looking at the same stars and, to my utter shame, tears began to roll down my cheeks.

I thanked God I was alone on duty. I couldn't bear the thought that a fellow comrade would see my pitiful tears and think of it as a sign of weakness. Such was the coldness of the night, the tears turned to ice on my face very quickly. The cold ones swiftly replaced by fresh set of warm ones.

I didn't know why I was crying or what was wrong with me,

I do know I felt so embarrassed by them that I wanted to hurl myself into the icy depths of the ocean until they stopped. At the time, it felt like it was the lowest point of my life, I couldn't understand what the hell the matter with me was.

I don't think I actually cared if I lived or died and that thought, in itself, angered me because so many people had been killed in this God awful war and I should have felt lucky to be alive. At some point the tears stopped flowing and I wiped my face with my handkerchief. Oddly, I seemed a little less on edge. It was as though unleashing my tears had relieved some of the intense pressure I constantly felt I was under. By the time my shift had finished I had sufficiently composed myself so that that no one aboard would have any idea how I was really feeling.

What continued to rile me was that I was supposed to be the man of the household and head of the family. I was meant to provide for and protect my family but I felt so very helpless, out in the middle of an ocean teeming with hidden dangers. It made me feel less of a man and I prayed to God that my family would all come through this war unscathed and promised Him that I would try and pull myself out of the murky pit that I found myself in if He would only keep everyone I loved safe.

23

Life in the Chinese camp was not dissimilar to life as a Japanese prisoner of war, apart from the fact that I was free. Food and water were always in short supply and anyone caught stealing would be tortured then killed. It was the only way to ensure the provisions were distributed evenly. I was so grateful to my saviours that I made a huge effort to integrate into their culture and way of life.

Zihao Son introduced me to other members of the fighting force. They taught me the words of the 'Red Flag', the song that was the Chinese National Anthem, and I felt privileged and proud to sing it among my fellow comrades. I learnt as much of the Chinese language as I could and was soon able to hold an adequate conversation in my new language. I was now known as 'Jian' which meant 'man of strength' in Chinese. I needed my rescuers to know that they had made the right decision to save me and that I would be an asset to the cause.

Guerrilla warfare was bloody and gruesome but at least I was a soldier fighting for a cause rather than a prisoner, broken and bent and inviting death. I gladly saluted the hammer and sickle flag of my adoptive country and was happy to join in with the communist songs we all sang. These people became my family and my lifelong friends and I wanted to help them in their fight against oppression and tyranny. I happily swore allegiance to the Chinese army and promised to fight to the death.

The evenings, when we were not on watch, Zihao would tell me all about the horrors of Shanghai and how his fellow man had suffered. He explained how the Chinese people were going about their business with no idea of the slaughter that was about to befall them. Out of nowhere, Japanese planes begun to fill the skies and bombard the unsuspecting city. Before long many residential areas had been turned it into rubble. Buildings that had stood for hundreds of years were now razed to the ground and, in some cases, with the inhabitants still inside.

Zihao cried bitter tears as he explained how the enemy had no care for the unarmed population living in Shanghai. The Japanese war machine had only one agenda, to kill, maim and invade. He told me how his two children aged five and seven had been blown into the air like ragdolls and killed instantly and how his wife had succumbed to her injuries a few days later. They had no warning that they would come under attack and no chance to get to safety.

I learned that the Japanese wanted Shanghai because of its port on the Yangtze River; it was the biggest port in China, therefore a central place which the Japanese were keen to have control of. The country was also rich in gas, rice and many other commodities. When China refused to surrender to the enemy, wave after wave of bombing followed, killing even more innocents. There was no talking or bargaining, just another appalling onslaught of destruction and slaughter.

Anger now replaced Zihao's tears. He explained that there was refuge, for some of his people, in an international settlement that Japan was afraid to attack but there was not enough room to offer most of the population sanctuary. Many terrified, defenceless souls were locked outside and left at the mercy of the enemy. Such was the annihilation and devastation wrought by the faceless foe, the people didn't stand a chance.

The ones that were not killed by the bombs lost their lives when one of the many burning buildings collapsed on them. Zihao spat into the mud as he shouted that it was deliberate mass murder and terrorisation of a blameless race of people.

I asked about the Geneva Convention and how Japan was allowed to bomb civilians. Zihao clarified what I already knew, that the Japanese were devoid of human emotion and did not honour the convention. He could not conceal his anger for an army that could kill and maim the defenceless. He understood acts of war were necessary but this was no act of war. It was cataclysmic slaughter and no human being should have to suffer as his family had.

Once the Japanese army had occupied Shanghai and killed anyone who got in their way, they split in a kind of crab-like pincer movement to cut off the retreat of the Chinese army. These were the militant soldiers who had formed their own militia and were desperately were fighting to defend what was left of the inhabitants of Nanking and the region itself.

I felt so much sadness for my great friend and horror when he explained that the blood crazed Japs had attacked an American gun boat, the USS Panay, killing many of the crew on board. Despite the vessels unique pattern indicating that it was an American boat, the craft was still bombed without warning or reason. As of yet the Americans were not an enemy of the invading force.

The Japanese insisted the bombing was a mistake and apologised. I didn't believe that they had attacked the craft in error and neither did anyone else who I spoke to. We were all in unanimous agreement the Japanese war machine would stop at nothing to invade and conquer. Zihao believed that Germany and Japan had to be stopped as they wanted to rule the entire world and I wholeheartedly agreed. I believe that if we allowed these mad men to conquer and rule, the world would become an unsafe place to live in.

Although the brave Chinese army fought valiantly to defend the Chinese republic, after a few days battle, the city fell to the Japanese army. Zihao went onto explain that during the occupation of Nanking, the population were raped, tortured, killed then butchered. Zihao estimated that up to 40 000 men, women and children were massacred. The enemy was not only happy with stealing a city they wanted to remove all proof of any of its inhabitants. This merciless, callous foe needed to be stopped. Zihao told me that China would never surrender and neither would I.

I made up my mind that I would never be taken prisoner again. I would rather die fighting for my cause than live under enemy rule. My days were methodical and strict, I carried out every order I was given, and volunteered for any job going. I was happy to protect what remained of the Chinese population who were now bravely rebuilding a new China in the West. This peaceful nation's bravery in the face of such cruel adversity humbled me to the core.

I felt on a par with these people because I too had been forced to flee the land of my birth by the Germans. My parents gave their lives so that my brother and I could escape and I felt that, in some small way, I was avenging their deaths because Germany and Japan fought on the same side. I often battled an inner rage at why some races were persecuted for no apparent reason other than the land of their birth or the religion they followed. It made no sense and sometimes I felt myself almost crushed by the sadness of so much unneeded loss of life.

I had been with the Chinese fighting force for just over three months when Zihao introduced me to his sister Ruolan. She and Zihao spent endless hours teaching me how to fight with only a razor sharp knife. Ruolan advised me to only use my rifle when absolutely necessary. She explained that we would only defeat the Japanese patrols only if we used the element of surprise. The noise of a gun would alert the enemy to our presence.

This was because the Japanese had more sophisticated weapons than we had and a bigger military force. So as soon as one of these patrols was spotted by one of our ever vigilant spies, we would camouflage ourselves to blend in with our surroundings then we would pounce on the unsuspecting foes. I enjoyed nothing more that the sight of sheer terror on the faces of these soulless men.

I lost count of the amount of throats I slashed when I was a soldier in China's guerrilla army. As time when on, the cracking sound the windpipe made as I split it wide open and the torrent of warm red blood, that spurted from the wound, no longer bothered me. I began to actually enjoy each kill and tot up the amount of slaughters I managed to do each month. The butchery became commonplace and was necessary to defeat the enemy. In my mind, to win against a race of barbarians, I needed to become one and that's exactly what I did.

I had been with the Chinese for around four months when Ruolan and I became lovers. I didn't feel as though I was being deceitful to my marriage with Lucy because it was not a love affair for either of us. It was much more complex than something as simple as a romance. We both needed the warmth and close companionship of another human being. Our sex was animal-like, in our desperate need for some type of normality in our murderous existence.

We lived for each day, as it dawned, because it was highly likely that we would not survive another. We would seek each other out whenever time allowed and hold onto one another as tightly as possible as our bodied merged into one. This seemed, to me, totally normal in the alien existence I was enduring and necessary if I was to survive and succeed in this hellish life.

25

I was in the middle of particularly gruelling night shift when the air raid siren screeched into life. I was so intent on the work I was doing, that what happened quite often, I nearly jumped out of my skin. Quickly, I grabbed my flask and net bag that contained my ration book, some family photos, my purse and some magazines. I called it my survival pack. This was because it contained important documents and I also found that flicking through a magazine or gazing at a photo somehow masked frightened I felt.

The inhabitants of the factory filed their way quickly, but in an orderly fashion, down into the large basement below the building. We had all tried to make it a less gloomy and uncomfortable space because we now seemed to be spending a lot of time down here. Together, the workers had put colourful cushions on the hard benches. The management had put a tea urn on a table in the far corner which we always ensured was filled with water. That way, if we were stuck down here for many hours we could, at least, now enjoy a cup of tea while we waited out the raid.

When the ominous hum of the enemy planes began to buzz some way off, I felt the usual stab of fear. I didn't think I would ever get used to it and the hot terror it injected in me. Each raid could mean the end of my life or that of someone I loved very much and constant anxiety pecked at me as I sat willing the attack to end.

As the noise grew in volume, Susan, Joyce and I huddled together for comfort. Susan, being the eldest of us all, talked gently to us, explaining how we were 'safe as houses' in the cellar. She cuddled Joyce and told her that the cellar had been here for centuries and would remain whole for many more to come.

A few months earlier Susan had confided to me that her estranged father, John Penhaligon, had recently moved to Bristol and she was terrified of the man. He had made her childhood a living nightmare when her mother had deserted them both when she was only seven years old.

Luckily, when her father had come looking for her, Susan was with Edward, her husband, and he had stood up to John Penhaligon and had told the man not to bother Susan unless she wanted him to.

She had no wish to clap eyes on the man ever again and was overjoyed that her father had obeyed Edward's request and had left her alone, much to her relief. I had mixed emotions regarding Susan's decision. Having no parents alive myself, as far as I knew, made me think that if a mother or father of mine ever materialised I would happily forgive and move on but I respected Susan's decision, only she knew how much she had suffered.

Any family, in my mind, was better than no family. Feeling totally alone in the world was a heady and scary existence. I was lucky I had Len and my daughters but I would have loved to have met some of my wider family. I often wandered if I had grandparents or aunties and uncles but I had no idea how to go about finding out. Still, if Susan decided to estrange herself from her father I wouldn't judge her because I felt it was not my place to. After a while, a small group of workers in the far corner began to sing a song and before long everyone in the building had joined in.

I could only just hear the singing above the thunderous noise of the planes but it made me smile, I turned to look at Susan and she grinned back at me. I could just about make out the words of 'Keep the Home Fires Burning" (Till the Boys Come Home), I joined in and immediately and felt a little less afraid ,as though we were actually telling Hitler to 'bugger off', and my mood turned more defiant than frightened. The next song was "A Bicycle Built for Two" followed by 'Run Rabbit Run. It was odd but singing had the uncanny method of diverting my terrified mind from what was going on inside it.

It was strange that belting out a few songs could totally change how I felt but it did. Even when the bombs landed so close that they shook the entire building making it moan and shudder, still we sang on louder still. We shook the concrete dust from our hair and rubbed it from our eyes. In my mind, it felt as though we were beating Adolf Hitler by not being scared. It was as though we were telling him that we would never bend to his tyranny and come what may, we would carry on fighting. I felt as though I belonged to an army of melodic patriots and together we would defeat the enemy.

It was a long raid and I was glad of a cup of tea to wet my dry throat and help the time pass a little quicker, just by enjoying the taste of a lovely cuppa. A couple of times, the few meagre lightbulbs that dimly illuminated the cellar flickered and failed and we were momentarily left in pitch darkness. This did unnerve me a little and I was extremely relieved when some candles were duly lit and placed at strategic points around the cellar. They weren't very bright but it was better than sitting in the choking blackness that felt as though it was suffocating me and crushing my ribcage.

There was audible gasp of relief when the 'all clear' finally sounded. We gathered up our belongings and stood up stiffly. I had been in one position for far too long and my legs didn't seem to be able to take my weight. I hobbled behind the rest of the factory staff, up the steep uneven steps into the glorious daylight of the factory floor, relieved once again that I had lived through another terrifying raid.

During the attack Susan and I had chatted and expressed our gladness that our beloved children were safe. Susan's two daughters, Edith and Iris were living in Cornwall with her in-laws and her husband Edward was fighting somewhere over-seas. We both missed their presence in our lives and fought hard to stave of the feelings of isolation and loss. To help each other through these trying times, any evenings that we both had off together we spent in each other's company. We would either visit the cinema or the Red lion pub, which was close to where we both lived.

I preferred the pub because it was made of solid granite so, in my mind, good enough to withstand any incendiar-ies the Germans dropped on. The cosy cellar underneath was perfectly equipped for an air raid. There was a gramophone player tucked into the corner on a rickety table with a choice of several records to play to help drown out he sounds of the bombs. I much preferred being in the pub when we were under attack, it felt much safer.

Being with other people always took my mind off what was going on and listening to music was calming and took my mind off what was happening outside. A few times, when Susan, Joyce and I had been watching a film at the cinema, the noise of the overhead planes were so loud that we could not hear the dialogue and had to abandon any attempts to watch the movie.

Also, at the pub, alcoholic drinks and tea were served so we could pretend that Hitler had not spoiled our evening at all, we'd merely relocated to the underground cellar. I had also heard, through the factory grapevine, how a cinema in town had been bombed and how, although the people in there looked as though they were uninjured, they were all dead in their seats. The bomb had sucked the air out of their lungs and the thought of this unnerved me and now made me wary of going to the pictures. I wondered if they had suffered at all but tried not to think about it too hard.

Thankfully, once the raid was over, we didn't have to continue our shift as it was now time for the night workers to arrive. I looked out for Edna but was surprised when I didn't see her because I knew it was her turn to work the nightshift. As I walked home I was shocked at what I saw because the bombs had sounded awfully close by. The factory and close surrounding areas had remained relatively untouched by the shelling. Susan and I linked arms as we made our way towards our homes.

I could smell the acrid odour of burning buildings some-where in the distance and it was so intense it burned my throat. I put my handkerchief up to my mouth as I made my way to my house. I'm not sure if this helped or not but I hoped it protected me from swallowing some of the minute particles of toxic dust. Susan did the same. I was glad the factory had escaped any damage. The government leaflets explained that it was in the country's best interest to keep the factories working wherever possible to ensure our fighting men had all the equipment they needed to win the war.

However, as I got further away from the factory and nearer to home, I realised that not everyone had been so lucky. Whole terraces had been turned into mounds of rubble and deep craters stood in place of the fallen buildings all along the roads and pavements. It made walking past them tricky and a little dangerous but neither of us complained because we were both happy to be alive. Susan and I manoeuvred our way around the obstacles before separating at the crossroads to go to our own homes.

When I turned the corner into Lavender Terrace, where my home was, however, I was momentarily paralysed by the scene in front of me. I stood, motionless, in a state of utter shock at the devastating scene that stood before me. Half of the Terrace was no more. Where the houses had once stood there was just a deep, wide hollow.

My tiny house was, miraculously, still standing but Edna's house was just rubble and dust which was blowing around the covered faces of the rescue workers. Her precious possessions were flapping around in the wind, for all and sundry to see and I knew that this would annoy her; she didn't like people nosing at her personal things. I quickly began to gather up some of her belongings to take to my home so she could collect them later.

Each of the rescue workers had a handkerchief or cloth of some sort tied around their mouth and nose to stop the thick grime getting into their throats. Such was the pall hanging over the area, even the ladies from the WVS had their faces covered as they served tea and biscuits to the survivors. I stood, for a while, surveying the charred remains of people lives and again wondered how this senseless killing could be justified.

I held onto Edna's red, gingham dust –covered tablecloth, which was now in need of a good soaking. The amount of filth almost obscured the pattern of the material. I began to collect some of her pots and pans and also a few items of her son's toys that were scattered about the place. Rescue workers and ARP wardens continued to move the rubble and masonry in silence in case anyone trapped could be heard shouting, while awaiting rescue.

I scanned the faces of the people to see if I could see Edna or any of her family, I couldn't. I guessed she must have gone to the shelter at the end of the street, at least I hoped she had. I shook myself suddenly because it felt as though an icy chill had travelled down through my whole body. I put Edna's bits and pieces on my own doorstep then walked towards the tea urn.

I turned to a woman who was busy handing out hot drinks. She wore a flower patterned pinafore wound around her whole body and tied at her waist. I asked her if she knew where the inhabitants of number twenty four, Edna's house, because I had some of their belongings to return to them.

The woman hastily finished serving tea to an exhausted salvage worker then came closer to me and grasped my hand. Her own hands were covered in grit and a sprinkling grey dust and she apologised. She swiped some tears off her dirty cheeks,

smearing grubby lines across the grime on her face then led me
to a chair that some kind soul had provided:

'My dear, all who lived at number twenty four have perished,'
She held my hands a little tighter as I looked at her like
she was some alien being who had dropped out of the sky,
she continued:

'Edna heard the air raid warning but told her neighbours
that she and the family wouldn't bother going to the shelter
because the tea was ready and she didn't want it going cold.'

Luckily the neighbour had made the wise decision to head to
the shelter otherwise she would have been in the same place as
Edna. I felt a semi blackness overcome me and then someone
pushed my head between my knees, though I don't know who
it was. A sickness washed over me and I shook myself to try
and regain some type of control over my body:

'I've got some of her things,' I mumbled, unable to grasp
the enormity of what the woman had just said.

I visualised each of faces of each of her little boys, including the baby, and I thought my heart would break. I couldn't
comprehend that Edna and her whole family had been wiped
out. She was always such a loud and jolly presence and everyone
in the street loved her; I couldn't help but smile as I remembered Edna saying, just a few weeks before:

'It'll take more than bloody Hitler to wipe my lot out',
she had laughed as she said it and was wearing the bright red
lipstick that she always wore.

The women worker had to leave me as there were so many
more people that needed her help and comfort. I understood
that she couldn't remain with me. I was still finding it hard to
believe what she said was actually true and kept looking out

for Edna and her brood. I was sure they would walk down the street at any minute.

Edna was so full of life and enthusiasm that I found it hard to comprehend that this beautiful, sunny lady had been snuffed out in a heartbeat. I tried to think what song we might have been singing when the bomb that destroyed her home and family was dropped but I couldn't, and what did it matter? Edna was dead, I had to face it.

I watched as the ARP wardens and Firemen and women began the painstaking job of looking for the bodies. I recognised one of the firefighters as John Penhaligon, Susan's father, partly from her description of him and partly because he was so much bigger than the other firemen. I guessed he was over six feet and was a stocky build with it. He, with all the other workers, gently pulled at the bricks and mortar and broken glass in the search for Edna and her children.

We all fell silent when a rescue worker put his finger to his lips, but the sound he heard was the hissing wheeze of a fractured gas pipe, not a breathing human being, no one actually believed that anyone was alive under the rubble but that did not stop us all from hoping and praying that someone had survived.

A crowd had now gathered and I guessed they must be friends or relatives of the people who once lived in the row of house next to Edna's that were now reduced to a deep hollow filled with wood and dust. Most of the women wore the same styled colourful, floral aprons that the WVS ladies wore and the bright colours were a startling contrast to the dreary grey scene in front of me.

An elderly woman approached the area, leaning heavily on a walking stick. I rose quickly and insisted that she sit on the chair that I had vacated. Her need to sit down was far greater than mine. As I looked into her tear-stained face it seemed that each line was deeply ingrained with sorrow.

I rested my arm around her shoulder and she patted my hand, absent-mindedly. It was as if she knew I was trying to offer her some comfort but I was not really helping to ease her heartache. We both watched the rescue operation. I felt a sense of helplessness nestle deep inside me as the work continued.

The dust finally began to settle when the first body was brought out. It was Edna's youngest, Dennis, who was just seven months old. He looked like a tiny porcelain doll; he was covered from head to toe in a thick blanket of grey/white cement particles. His soft downy hair was stuck to his head and his tiny eyelids were shut. John Penhaligon lifted out and the tiny child then clambered over the rubble.

I watched as the burley fireman struggled carefully over the wreckage carrying the tiny, lifeless bundle. He placed little Dennis down gently, on the grubby pavement, and let tears fall unchecked from his sorrow-filled eyes. John's arms then fell open and he looked skyward as though he was asking God why this had happen to a little boy who was so young and innocent. The sight of the big man crying, without an ounce of embarrassment, made me feel as though I couldn't breathe because of the profound grief that seeped into the depth of my soul.

Dennis was wearing the blue matinee jacket that I had knitted for him before he was born. I had pulled apart an old jumper of my own and Edna loved the delicate lengths of blue ribbon I had woven through the garment to tie it onto the little lad. It was now filthy and torn. The baby's tiny fists were covered by the sleeves and I prayed that the little boy had not suffered and that death had come quickly.

One by one the family were lifted out from under from their collapsed home. The big firemen cried over every body. When they lifted Ronnie, Edna's eldest son out, I could see that he still held his catapult in his hand. He was a mischievous little imp who Edna had given several 'clips around the ear' to for firing the thing at a passing policeman.

Poor Ronnie, he would never grow old or become a father. John Penhaligon tenderly wiped the dust from each little face as he laid them down. Edna's husband was lifted out and quickly wrapped in a blanket to hide the fact that the top half of his body was not connected to the bottom half.

Finally they pulled Edna out. Her scarf had fallen from her head and her peroxide blonde hair was now streaked grey with grime and dust. The angle at which her head lay told me that her neck was broken. As the filth was gently rubbed from her face, I caught a glimpse of her red lipstick smeared across her lips, and the pain became almost unbearable. As the family's bodies were loaded into a van to be taken to the hospital, I quickly raced over and bent down to kiss Edna's cold cheek. I told her that I loved her and would miss her.

I watched the vehicle, carrying my dear neighbour and her wonderful family, drive away. I wanted to see them all take their final journey in this world so I watched until they were out of my sight. When there was nothing left to see, not even smoke belching from the exhaust pipe, I turned and walked towards my own house. The bewilderment I felt was indescribable. I put the kettle on but I felt as though I was a robot, just going through the motions. I felt empty inside as though I was another person watching my every move.

I heard a knock on the door but I didn't go to it. I just stood, leaning against the oven and getting comfort from its warmth. The kettle whistled that it was ready and I slid it off the hob without realising that I done it. The front room door opened and there stood Susan. I was so relieved to see her. She rushed forward and pulled me into her arms. I cried until there were no tears left inside me.

A short time later, when my tidal wave of grief had turned into gentle ripple, we prepared an evening meal together. What else could we do but carry on? Susan listened as I told her about Edna and her rowdy family and how kind she always was. At the time it felt to me that the pain of my loss would never go away and I was so grateful for Susan's friendship at a time when I needed it so very much.

Time marched on and it was true what everyone told me. The agony did lessen and I began to think of all the happy times Edna and I had spent together and any tears that threatened when a picture of her lovely face crept into my mind unexpectedly decreased with each day. Life continued and the war raged on and we all got through as best we could.

Susan and I were sitting in my cosy kitchen a few weeks later when, out of the blue, my lovely husband, Leonard walked in, with his kitbag slung over one shoulder. I could not have been more overjoyed to see him and flew into his arms. We held each other and kissed until Susan, clearing her throat loudly, reminded us that she was in the room.

I blushed and apologised then introduced Len to Susan. Len walked towards Susan ready for a handshake but Susan quickly pulled him into a tight embrace. I was happy, these were two of the most important people in my life and I wanted them to like each other. Susan picked up her coat as if to leave:

'You don't have to go Susan,' I told her quickly, we had planned an evening at the pub.

'I'm not playing gooseberry to you two lovebirds,' she said, as she grinned widely, ' We see each other all the time, you spend whatever time you can with your gorgeous husband and I'll go and meet Joyce in the Red lion,'

She pulled the door after herself and was gone. I turned to face Len and suddenly felt shy and awkward like teenagers on our first date. I looked down and smiled when I realised that Len was feeling the same way. I made us a cup of tea and we sat down to chat. It was then I became aware that Len was not the same as he usually was. He seemed as though he was drunk because his speech was slightly slurred but I couldn't smell any alcohol:

'You seem different Len?' I questioned, looking into his eyes but he couldn't seem to focus on mine. He shuffled his feet nervously.

'Tell me Len, what's the matter, maybe I can help.' I lent close and held his hand. I watched as he ran his fingers through his thick hair, he was obviously ill at ease with what he was going to tell me and I silently prayed that he had not met some other woman on his travels. I braced myself for this, just in case I was right. When Len began to speak I was relieved and surprised at the same time:

'On board ship,' he hesitated, and then began again. 'On board ship I felt a kind of miserableness descend on me and I couldn't shake it off, then it turned into some kind of panic, lie a big ball of fright in the middle of my stomach, I wanted to physically put my hand in and tear it out.'

A tear fell down his cheek and I stood up and put my arms around him and told him to carry on:

'I kept having screaming nightmares and waking the rest of the crew up, I couldn't get the sight of my parents being murdered by the baying mob out of my head. Stupid noises, like a seagull screeching would make me hit the deck and lie there in a trembling mess. I went to see the doc, he prescribed some tablets but they make me feel woozy, I can't go back to the way I was.'

My heart felt as though it was breaking as I listened to Len. My big, strong man sounded as broken and fragile as a tiny bird. I held him close as I tried to think of a way to help him:

'It's ok to cry Len, its nature's way of letting your emotions out instead of letting them fester inside you, no one has to see you,'

I took a breath:

Also, I don't think the medication is very good for you, love, dulling your mind won't make all that has happened go away, it's better to face your feelings head on.'

Len looked up as if he was about to protest:

'Let me finish love,' I continued, 'keep taking the medication if you want but its only masking the actual problem, no matter how long you take it, the hurt will still be there. Why don't you stop taking it gradually then every time you have a feeling of panic or fear write it down, exactly how you feel. Then the next time you're on leave, we'll sit down and read it together and talk the feeling through? Come on, it's got to be better than walking around in a semi trance, will you give it a go?' I finished.

'What about the nightmares and waking up the other lads, that's not fair on them?' Len muttered:

'I'm sure that once you start writing down what you feel, it will help and the nightmares will gradually stop, until they do, say sorry to the chaps and ask them to improvise some ear plugs, they are your mates after all,' I said then smiled widely at him:

'Ok, I'll give it a go,' Len agreed. 'It does feel like I'm walking around with a padding of cotton wool wrapped around my head,' he laughed.

Len and I spent the rest of his leave together, getting to know one another again. I showed him photos of our daughters and promised him that on his next leave we would go over to Ireland to see them. I went to the train station with Len to see him off, at the end of his three day leave.

He seemed so much better than he was when he first arrived and I could only hope that being back on the convoys would not put his recovery back too far. My heart ached for him and all that he was going through, I cursed Hitler for his bloody war and prayed to God that it would be over soon.

I could not, however, help Len over his worry for Michael. We were constantly being told that *no news was good news* but I didn't believe this about Michael. We had two post cards from when he was first captured by the Japanese some eighteen months ago. For the last year no one had heard any word. For me, that did not bode well. Every friend I knew who had a husband who was a prisoner of war received some kind of communication, even if it was just a hastily scribbled not on a scrap of people to let them know that their loved one was still alive.

I was absolutely certain that Michael would write if he could so why hadn't he? Lucy seemed surprisingly unconcerned about this lack of communication. I knew she had been spoiled as a child, before her fall from grace, and I think that this was what helped her through. She believed that nothing else bad would happen to her because her parents had brought her up to believe that it wouldn't, I could only hope she was right.

She seemed to have put the trauma she suffered with the loss of her son right out of her mind, as though it had never happened. I guessed this was maybe the way she coped and I hoped it helped her get through whatever life had to throw at her. I, myself, could never do that. Everything that happened in my life affected me in some small way and I was not physically capable of 'forgetting' it or putting it into a corner of my mind where I didn't think about. I believed that memories of past events paved the way for future ones and holding onto them made me stronger and able to face life's obstacles.

I tried my best to remain upbeat and to grieve when I was alone. The people around me certainly didn't need someone so wrapped up in their own misery that they didn't care how it affected the moral of the rest of the work force. Bristol seemed dreary now Len was gone. I missed the warmth of his body in bed at night and the comfortable companionship that we both shared. As I walked, miserably, back from the train station I couldn't fail to miss the devastation of my once beautiful city.

Complete terraces had been flattened by enemy bombs. Amongst the rubble tiny weeds began to grow and I wondered how they had manged to flourish amongst the debris that was once a person's home. Most of the many hotels that were dotted around the city had either been closed for the duration or had been commandeered by the government. It seemed that ever property had been touched by the war in some way and I longed for the time before the war began. I yearned for the simple hopes and dreams that we all had then.

I wanted to watch my family grow without fear and see my daughters mature into adults with families of their own. Now, I was unsure if any of us would live through this time of destruction and death. A sense of gloom washed over me as I made my way to work. I now had an inkling of how my dear Len must feel and thought, maybe, I was a little too hasty in advising him to come off his medication. If it helped to get him through the dark days ahead, who was I to tell him to stop?

I quickly gently shook my head and mentally reprimanded myself. Poor Len was in constant danger and no one had a clue where Michael was and here I was feeling sorry for myself because I was missing him when he had only been gone for five minutes. There were many wives and sweethearts in the same position as me and they just got on with life, as I should do. At least my Len was alive, for now a least.

I comforted myself with the knowledge that Hester and Daisy were in a place of safety with a member of my own family caring for and loving them. I was a lot better off than some people and should jolly well be grateful. It was with this thought that I arrived at my work bench and began my day's work.

26

In June we suffered our worst setback since 1937, when the Japanese invaded in 1942. We lost the Burma Road which was New China's only route of getting supplies and weapons. Still, mine and my fellow freedom fighter's courage never wavered. We launched a counter attack against our murderous enemy. We raced down from the mountains and swept upon the Japanese invaders like a swarm of locust. After a courageous fight and many lives lost, we cheered as we watched the Japanese army's hasty withdrawal and the pride and absolute joy we felt was enormous.

The battle of *Changsia* was another battle that boosted anyone's flagging morale's for all of us and one I was sure would go down in history. It was one of the bloodiest conflicts but we won. It did not matter that, as a country, we fought alone and would continue until we were a free land once more.

We made a pact between us that we would never yield to the invading army. We did not want to live in a country that was not free from tyranny. It would be another two years before the Americans joined us in a united force against the Japanese. Sadly I would be too battle weary and radicalised to realise who was a friend or who was a foe.

Both Ruolan and I were truly surprised when Ruolan became pregnant. We had tried to be careful and protect against an unwanted pregnancy. Neither of us wanted to bring a child into a world at war but now there was nothing to be done about it, it had happened. I tried to persuade Ruolan to go to a place of safety while she was carrying our baby but she refused and continued to fight.

It was one of my greatest joys to be present when Ruolan pushed my baby daughter into the world. She was born a little early in December 1942 but was perfect in every way. Also present at the birth was Ruolan's cousin, Wenling. Contrary to the typical Chinese physique for an eastern woman, Wenling was tall and heavily built and, I thought, quite masculine in her ways but she had a big heart and I loved her dearly.

All of the other Chinese ladies I had met were dainty and small in stature but they all had the souls of warriors. Even Wenling, with her manly habits, could not stop a few tears falling as she held Ruolan's hand as she gave birth. She and Ruolan were very close owing to the fact that they had lost many family members during the invasion of Shanghai and the continuing bombardment of its citizens. At that moment, as the three of sat huddled together in the tiny tent; I actually felt a part of their little family.

I cried tears of sheer elation when I looked at the new life Ruolan and I had created. The tiny child had jet black hair and bright blue eyes. Her little hands were bunched into fists as she screamed her way into the world, only ceasing when Ruolan put the infant to her breast. I felt an overwhelming feeling of contentment as I watched Ruolan smile down at our new born daughter. I swore to myself that I would never forget that moment for the rest of my life but, sadly, it was to be erased from my memory in the passage of time.

We spent three precious days together as a family. We decided to name our beautiful daughter, Triun - pronounced Tree-Un, a mixture of trinity and unity in the hope that her birth would bring peace to the world. Ruolan told me of her pride in the Chinese people. She explained how they were a peaceful nation and Japan had just expected them to surrender. They could not, however, do this after the barbarism that was meted out to her fellow countrymen.

She told me how millions of people had travelled west to start the New China and how the country traded space for time. Her bright eyes shone as she told me how they needed a road into their new country for supplies and weapons and how the allies had told them that building it would take six or seven years to complete. China knew they could not be without the thoroughfare for that amount of time. Ruolan was part of a united republic that built the road to Burma in less than a year with sweat, toil, blood and tears.

At the beginning, as the Chinese fled the bloodshed, they used every river or track pointing westwards. Each and every person was heavily laden with supplies and building provisions. Every sandbank and barge was pressed into service. Any railways that were built were pulled up and destroyed after they had used them so the enemy could not follow them. My admiration for my adopted country grew with every story I was told and with every act of heroism I witnessed

Ruolan told be about the that libraries, schools and hospitals that had been dismantled from the bombed remains of Shanghai and carried to the new city by whatever means there was. Sandstone cliffs on which the city was built were constructed into caves by a workforce of thousands for the people to shelter from air raids. It was the sheer number of willing volunteers that ensured a New China was built and protected. Ruolan went on to explain with tears of pride welling in her eyes.

As I listened to her obvious respect for her compatriots I could not help but wonder what had happened to the world. I could not understand why one man would want to kill another, let alone a women or a child. I began to feel as though I was losing some of my humanity along the way, on my fight for freedom. When I was first rescued by my Chinese comrades, I would wake screaming in the night, having dreamed about gouged eyes and burning, tortured bodies but these dreams soon disappeared.

As the months dragged on, and despite the enduring efforts of our Japanese enemy to destroy the newly built city, they were unsuccessful. Ruolan explained that, unknown to the enemy, all the thriving factories were underground and worked day and night to produce weapons to fight the adversary. Her people would never surrender and they anticipated the Japanese army's every move and continued to stand fast. The province of Chunking became a symbol of the nation's imperishable life force.

When my daughter, Triun, was three days old, she and Ruolan left the camp for the safety of the West. A mother's instinct to protect her young was too strong to for Ruolan to stay and fight. I was relieved that Ruolan would no longer be amongst the fighting force and that our child would be out of danger. I also knew that I would miss them both very much but that was an easy price which I happy to pay to keep my family safe.

Ruolan had left six days earlier and it had been quite an uneventful week. Most of my time was spent foraging for food and keeping my ever present weapon clean and ready for use. This particular evening, however, the respite was broken and an enemy patrol was spotted lurking a little way from our base. I raced to my allocated spot and knelt down and looked through the site of my gun. I could make out about half a dozen armed figures and as I peered closer I could clearly see the face of the enemy.

I slowly took aim as one of the soldiers turned to face me. It was as though he could feel my presence because I was sure he couldn't actually see me. I was heavily camouflaged and hidden low down into a shallow dugout. I had pulled the surrounding foliage, which had been cut down at an earlier time, over me and my fellow men. I knew that there was not a chance that the enemy could see any of us in our present position. The landscape was familiar to me but not to the enemy which gave us the advantage and therefore the best chance of winning.

As I peered at the Japanese soldier, through the raised site of my gun, I realised that the enemy was only just a boy. It seemed to me that he had the soft skin of a child, not the rugged face of a killer. The sight threw me, momentarily, I wondered if I had become as bloodthirsty as the enemy if I was prepared to shoot a child. Then I reminded myself that I was not the aggressor in this war and that I had to keep fighting for everything I stood for.

A flicker of light caused the boy to look right in my direction. I felt as though his eyes were looking directly into mine.

I saw the terror on his face and the tears he began cry. I could do nothing. I took aim and shot him in the temple. He fell instantly to the ground, throwing his rifle behind him. The tears continued to drip from his open eyes and a vision of his family came into my head. I imagined his mother going mad with grief and his father vowing to avenge his killer.

I pondered over the suffering I had caused another person's family but was unable to see what else I could do. It was a case of shoot or be shot. If the enemy overran us and made it to new China, there was not a shred of doubt, in my mind, about what they would do to its inhabitants, including Ruolan and Triun. The only thing I could do was fight and kill any aggressor that threatened all those I held dear. Once the patrol was silent, we crept closer, ever vigilant to ensure there were no enemy soldiers left alive.

We had done our job well. There were no survivors. All members of the platoon were dead. I looked at their faces as I leant over and kicked any weapons close to the bodies, out of enemy reach. I was sure not one of these men could have been over the age of twenty.

I came across the lad that I had killed and felt compassion for him and sadness at the life I had taken away from him. I leant over and gently closed his eyes and muttered a small prayer, under my breath, for his safe passage into the next world. I knew he was just following orders from faceless bureaucrats, as we all were. His fight was now over but mine still continued.

That night, as I struggled to sleep, the boy's lifeless, tear-stained face constantly penetrated my dreams. I awoke screaming for forgiveness when I dreamt that he was begging me not to shoot him and pleading for my help. I quickly swiped my shameful tears from my face and turned to face the other way in an effort to purge his face from my mind.

His image did not leave willingly but continued to disturb both my waking and sleeping hours. I was unsure as to why this particular kill had affected me anymore than the dozens of others I had carried out and waited patiently until the nightmares ceased and his face dissolved into nothing.

27

December 5 1942
VIOLET

I'd noticed that Susan, my dear friend, was becoming close to an American airman called Jimmy Fairly. They had met up some seven months earlier when Jimmy had just arrived in England. We had come across the frightened man as the air raid siren rang out some months earlier; he had become separated from the rest of his crew and was terrified and staring madly about, unsure what to do or where to go. Susan had taken him under her wing and led him to the nearest Anderson Shelter.

I watched them show each other black and white photos of their respective children and was glad to see Jimmy visibly relax a little. Susan later confided in me that what had started out as an innocent friendship between two lonely people had blossomed into a romance. I was alarmed because Susan was playing a very dangerous game in these perilous times.

I was stunned when Susan told me and warned her to be very careful. Her husband Edward had been away fighting for the last eighteen months and if Susan was found out, she would be vilified by everyone who knew her. I did, however, understand how she felt. The constant loneliness never left me as I lived through this bloody war. My family were torn apart and living in different countries, it was a demanding time for everyone.

Still. I couldn't help but worry about where the relationship would lead to.

I myself couldn't imagine cheating on Len but I didn't want to be judgemental to Susan, I was far from perfect. I also knew that Susan's father John Penhaligon had died a few months earlier. He had committed suicide by jumping into the Clifton Gorge. Susan did not seem to be upset by his death but maybe it had hurt her deep inside and that's why she found comfort in the arms of the handsome American airman. Susan had helped me through some of my darkest times and I would help her too, if and when, she needed me.

Today, as we sipped our Sherries in the Red Lion Pub, I noticed that Susan was looking tired and drawn and as though her mind was elsewhere. There were constant frown lines engraved into her forehead and she was smoking far more cigarettes than she usually did. I held her hand, under the table and asked her quietly, if there was anything she wanted to talk about. Susan looked into my eyes:

'I'm pregnant,' she whispered, as she gazed at the grubby floor.

I really thought my heart might stop beating; such was my shock at Susan's confession. For her, this was a true disaster. Everyone would know that this baby was not Susan's husbands and I now understood why she looked the way she did and was sorry for the dilemma she found herself facing. Susan went onto explain there was a chink of light at the end of her long, dark tunnel of misery.

She told me how her estranged mother had offered to bring up the baby as her own. However, Susan had nowhere to go once the pregnancy started to show, she had no one to turn to and was at her wits end. She confided in me that she'd even thought about following her father and jumping into Clifton Gorge to save everyone she loved any heartache. I squeezed her hand as she spoke and told her to put those thoughts out of her head and we would sort her problem out somehow.

She went onto explain that Jimmy had been stationed elsewhere and did not know about the baby, she had no way of tracking him down because she wasn't related to him. Also, both she and Jimmy had decided that their affair had to end as they both had families that they loved. Jimmy had a wife Maria back home and a three year old son named Donnie. I felt such pity for Susan as she quickly swiped away a single tear that ran down her pale face.

Susan's torment was palpable and I worried that she might actually do what her father had done and take her own life if someone didn't help her. She explained that she was now five months pregnant but such was the constant worry gnawing away at her that she had been unable to eat and actually lost weight rather than gaining it.

I now noticed how gaunt her face was and how her once rounded cheek bones stuck out of her ashen face. She was wearing clothes two sizes too big for her in the hope that she could conceal the pregnancy; it was working at the moment, because I had not guessed and we were as close as sisters, but I knew time was running out. I wracked my brain to try and think of a solution to Susan's plight. I knew there must be something I could do. Too many lives were at stake if I couldn't help her.

Suddenly, like a shining beacon in a black night, Lucy, my sister-in-law's face came into my mind and I began to form a plan. I was sure she wouldn't mind helping Susan. After all, she had suffered her own unwanted pregnancy so I was sure she would know exactly what Susan was going though and how she must be feeling. I explained my idea to Susan and for the first time in a long while I saw a tinge of colour come into her cheeks.

Both of us huddled tightly together as I relayed to Susan what had happened to Lucy. As we walked home from the pub, later that evening, Susan hugged me tightly and thanked me several times. I told her that that was what friends were for and her tears threatened to rain down once more. I really hoped Lucy would agree to help, I was sure that she would but I couldn't be absolutely positive and I wished I had asked her first before telling Susan and giving her hope.

The following day I sent an urgent telegraph to Lucy and asked her to telephone me at my place of work as soon as she had received it. I outlined the importance of how quickly she should contact me then said a hasty prayer imploring her to help. The day after I posted my correspondence, I waited, keeping half an eye on the factory foreman, silently urging him to call me into the office to answer my urgently awaited call.

Bless my dear Lucy, she must have raced down to the telephone box and called me the minute she received my letter. I quickly and quietly told Lucy about Susan's predicament. As I expected, Lucy said she would be happy to have Susan stay with her as long as she needed. I let out a huge sigh of relief and rushed off to find Susan.

Two days later, I waved her off on the train to Southampton. She already looked a lot better and I was glad that I had been able to help her. Her next step would be to catch a ferry to Ireland and she would stay there for the rest of the pregnancy. The plan was she would then bring the child back to England for her mother to care for. Susan told me that she would never forget my kindness and would repay me in any way she could. I was just happy to help my dear friend in one of her darkest moments. Living life through a world war was hard enough without more of life's trials and tribulations adding to our general worries.

28

March 13 1943
MICHAEL

Living in the dense juggle could only be described as prime-val at worst and basic at best. I'd been here for more than a year now and could not remember the last time I'd worn a pair of shoes. The soles of my feet now resembled old leather and I ran through the jungle as though I'd been born here. Shoes were a commodity that I no longer needed. In my mind, I felt as though I had put my real life on hold for the duration of the war. I could not decide if I would have to resume my previous existence if a time came when the world was at peace.

I now knew how to hunt down a wild animal. I could skin, gut and cook the meat over an open fire. Nothing of the animal was wasted. It was a similar task to hunting down the Japanese patrols; it was to enable us to survive. We would mask our faces and bodies with whatever nature had at hand when the mission needed us to. When we went out to hunt we would become similar to the eerie night shadows that no one could be sure existed.

Sometimes I found it hard to differentiate between the wild-life and the enemy. I was terrified of the Burmese python that slithered silently around the jungle. It seemed to me that it was acutely alert to its killing power; although it wasn't venomous it was strong enough to crush a man to death in minutes. The stealthy, quiet demeanour of the animal reminded me most of our Japanese foes, both were ruthless and merciless whenever they felt the need to be.

I also learned that the tapir was a sort of wild pig and it made a tasty supper if I was lucky enough to catch one. The only way to trap this animal was with the element of surprise. If the animal spotted me before I saw him, it was fifty-fifty chance between who would die first. Tapirs fought to the death so it was a risky business but very rewarding. The taste of the Tapir reminded me of the roast pork I used to eat at home in Ireland.

There were also creatures known as flying foxes that were so enormous that when I first saw one, I dived for cover. I estimated their wingspan to be more than five feet wide and although they enjoyed wild berries and were not carnivorous, I couldn't be sure which one of us would win in a fight. These graceful creatures unnerved me and I was very weary whenever I spotted one. They were like nothing I had ever seen before back home.

Food and water were always in short supply so hunger was a constant companion for me and my comrades. In my mind, I actually became a Chinese warrior; I was no longer a Jewish Soldier. My family back home in Ireland became remote and I struggled to picture them. Because there was no correspondence, I wandered if they had written me off as dead.

I wouldn't blame them. At least when I was a prisoner of war, there had been a stunted supply of letters, now there was nothing. I was glad that Lucy had Gerta to talk to; I hated to think that she might be lonely.

I had seen Ruolan a few times since she had returned to the safety of the West. She showed me a photo of my little daughter. She was now a chubby little baby with beautiful smile and wide dark eyes. I wanted to see some of my own features when I looked at my child's face but she seemed to look very much like Ruolan. Here in the jungle, these people were now my family. I had no idea how long I would remain here or if I would get out alive.

When Triun was three months old, Ruolan left her with friends in New China and returned to fight for her homeland. It was with mixed feelings that I greeted her. I was happy to see her but also feared for her safety. She was, however, her own person and I had no right to tell her what to do.

All I could do was continue the fight for survival and hope that everyone I loved was safe from harm. As I sat on watch duty, one balmy March evening, the stillness of the night made me feel as though I was the only person in the world. I knew that the man who left Ireland to fight in the war was an alien to me.

I could not recognise what I had become. It was as though I had split myself into two different people. One was the placid man who liked to watch the wild birds flying above in the beautiful Irish sky and the other was a ruthless guerrilla fighter who would rip a man's throat out in the blink of an eyelid.

I felt that Lucy was a part of another life that I no longer belonged to and I hoped that, if I made through the war, I would be able to make a life with Ruolan and Triun in New China. We had now talked about this and both agreed that this was our future. I didn't tell Ruolan about Lucy because, in my mind, she was from another world and not part of ours.

I didn't know if Lucy had moved on and found someone else. If she believed I was dead, this would be the natural thing to do. I had no way of communicating with her and vice versa. We were separated by thousands of miles and poles apart in the ways we lived our lives.

One night in late March, as I vigilantly watched the darkened landscape, the peaceful silence of the evening was broken by the quietest of sounds. It was only the slightest of noises, like the snapping of a twig but I was immediately alert and in fighting mode. I slid onto my belly, as lithe the Burmese python, and made myself as invisible, as I could, to the approaching enemy. I rubbed mud onto my face and pulled loose foliage over my body to blend in with countryside around me.

I then made a deep, cackling noise that could have come from any of the wild beasts in the jungle but one that I knew my comrades would understand. Looking through my gun site, I strained my eyes and looked into the open space about ten feet in front of me and saw what I was looking for. I calculated that there were at least twenty Japanese soldiers in the scouting patrol. I could tell by their movements and bodily reactions that they were unaware they were being watched. The laughed jovially as they started to build a fire to cook a meal on, unaware it would be their last one ever.

I felt the minute small movement of another body, next to mine, and turned to see Zihao beside me, he was soon joined by Aiguo, a young Chinese boy who was still attending school when Shanghai was invaded and who had lost many family members, also present was his father, Chongan. Some minutes later we were joined by Ruolan and her cousin Wenling. All of us were as invisible as the dim shadows. Wenling was a great asset to our team; she was easily the height and build of western man but had the quiet common sense that all women seemed to have.

When I first encountered the Japanese enemy, I thought of them as inhuman and invincible but now I knew that this was their exterior persona to frighten any adversaries they may encounter. In reality they were not dissimilar to us. As had we, they had been forced to fight in a war that was not of their making, but that did not mean that I had one ounce of compassion for them. I knew they would show none for me. The law of the jungle was to kill or be killed and it was a law that I always obeyed.

One of the enemy patrol guards began walking towards where we were all hidden. I put my hand up to alert the others of this. I was sure that the man merely needed to urinate and had no idea we were there. If we were to be the victors in each battle, it was important that the enemy was all in one place so we could surround and ambush them. Surprise attacks always worked best.

At a crucial point, the moon slid from behind a cloud, just for a moment, but in that time the Japanese soldier spotted the glint of Ruolan's silver bracelet. It belonged to her mother and she always wore it. We were no longer hidden; the man started screaming as he buttoned his trousers:

'Ee-yah, arimasu teki.'

I knew this roughly translated to, 'no, you enemy' and also that if we did not act now we would become the hunted, not the hunters. I gave the order to open fire and we immediately sent a volley of bullets towards the Japanese patrolmen. I watched as some dropped like skittles and others reached, feverishly for their weapons.

I revelled in the intense panic that showed on the facial expressions of these battle-hardened men. They were nothing, just pawns in their emperor's game, as we were. Every time one of their bodies thudded to the ground I felt a rush of adrenalin race through me followed by a passionate emotion of intense happiness. Each kill was like a stripe on my sleeve or a medal on my chest.

Finally the screaming stopped and bodies lay strewn across each other. I rose and walked slowly towards the corpses. I knew the Japs would happily 'play dead' by lying under the bodies of their fellow man, until we approached, then they would turn and shoot us between the eyes. They had tried it many times, now we all knew their agenda and advanced with the utmost caution. My eyes were fixed on the figures on the ground and my weapon was raised in readiness.

One by one, I stabbed the prostrate figures with my bayonet. Not until I was sure that they were all dead did I give the order for the rest of my party to emerge from their hiding places. As I did, they all came forwards with the same cautiousness as I had. I turned my back to the enemy and smiled at Ruolan and that was when the shot rang out. It was so close I felt the wind as it it whistled past my ear.

I watched, as if in slow motion the shell tear through the air and hit Ruolan just above the bridge of her nose. For a second she looked shocked then afraid and then she was dead. I turned around towards the filthy adversary and saw who had murdered my love. A young boy, who I guessed could not have been more than seventeen or eighteen years old. He was grinning widely as he lay on the rough ground.

He was bleeding heavily from a gaping wound in his stomach and his breathing was laboured and uneven. I advanced towards the boy. His face was still twisted into a gloating smirk. I don't know what I turned into at the precise moment but it was then that I realised the old Michael was no longer alive. I dropped to my knees and shoved my stiletto blade knife into the boys gaping wound.

I smiled with pleasure as the lad no longer smirked but screeched with great agony as I twisted the blade inside his writhing body. Now it was my turn to smirk. Tears rolled down the dying soldiers face; before he died I put a knife through his eyes and another through his genitals. His suffering warmed my heart as I watched as the life slowly seeped out of him. Tears of blood wept from his bloodied eyes. I looked at the contorted features of my latest kill and was happy that he had suffered before he died.

In my mind, I believe that was the exact point that I lost any humanity that remained within me. I walked over to Ruolan and looked into her beautiful face. I closed her eyes for the final time then relieved her of her weapons. I was glad that her war was now over but sorrow-filled that I would never hold her in my arms again. Although I was dying inside, my outer facial expression didn't change.

I ordered the men to pick up Ruolan's body and carry it back to camp so we could perform a hasty burial. I then doused the Japanese patrol with paraffin and set them alight. I lingered, for a little too much time, as I watched them burn then turn to ash.

29

VIOLET

Less than three months after she left, Susan returned home in the dead of the night and took her baby to her mother's home. She had given birth to a little girl who she called, Jane. Susan smiled as she described the tiny child's blonde hair and porcelain skin. Although there was an inner sadness hiding behind Susan's eyes, she and I both knew that her daughter living with her mother was the best possible outcome and that she was very lucky.

Only a few weeks after Susan had given birth, her mother-in-law called the factory and said that Susan was urgently needed at home, at Carmarthen farm. I told the lady the first thing that came into my mind, that Susan was visiting sick relatives in Ireland. I immediately regretted it when the woman said that Susan didn't have any relatives in Ireland. In a panic, I quickly replaced the receiver. I then sent Susan a telegram, relaying the message to her.

Susan's young daughter was around three months old when, once more, as it grew into an increasingly regular event, the air raid siren rang out in the middle of the work day. We all filed down to the cellar as quickly as possible wondering if this war would ever end and we would no longer have to endure the terror of an enemy air raid. Thankfully the attack was a short one and we were soon making our way out into the bright sunlight.

I squinted as the daylight almost blinded me. The factory seemed to be unharmed with just a small crack in one of the end walls. We all waited while the foreman checked around the structure of the factory to ensure it was safe for us to return to work. It was vital that we did this as soon as was humanly possible. If the war was to be won, production had to be kept going.

As we enjoyed a brief respite from our daily toil, Susan's mother arrived pushing little Jane in her pram. Susan walked over and politely asked if she could hold the baby, she then brought her over to show me with a proud smile spread across her face. Joyce joined us and some other co-workers as we all began to drawl over the tiny little girl.

Suddenly, a sprinkling of dust covered us all and to my horror, I looked up to see the end wall falling towards the whole group of us. Susan, a few others and I instantly raced back towards the safety of the factory. We didn't quite make it inside and I screamed as I heard the roar of the masonry falling.

I covered my ears and buried my face into my arms and waited until the roaring noise stopped and silence enveloped us. I tentatively looked around as my eyes became accustomed to the gloom. All of us were all covered in a coating of cement dust and Susan was desperately trying to clear her baby's nose and mouth. Susan had leaned over her baby and taken most of the grime on her back and shoulders but some still landed on Jane.

I looked around to try and decipher what had happened and then it became clear. The damaged wall had toppled over but had stayed in one piece and was now leaning against the solid factory wall. We were all entombed in a triangular shaped space. As my eyes grew more used to the dimness, I could also make out the shape of Joyce and a few other workmates. We were the lucky ones, we had chosen to run, the ones that didn't were buried underneath the rest of the wall. I heard Joyce begin to whimper and groped my way over to her:

'Don't worry Joyce,' I reassured her, 'the rescue party are already on their way so we won't be trapped for long.' I crossed my fingers behind my back because I had no idea if rescue was imminent or not:

'What if the wall doesn't hold and falls on us all,' she sobbed:

'If it was going to fall, it would have done by now,' I told her, sternly, but again I was unsure if what I was saying was true or not.

Joyce nodded and blew her nose in her overall, she clearly believed everything I said and I could only hope that I was right. As the dust settled, the visibility improved and I could now see who I was actually trapped with and how many of us there were. I over looked at Susan; she was looking down at her baby with an expression of pure love and devotion. I turned to see Joyce looking in Susan's direction also and knew, by the look in her eyes, that she knew Jane was Susan's baby. I hoped to God that she would keep Susan's secret.

We sat and chatted amongst ourselves. At different times, one of us needed a hug or someone to hold our hand to help us get through the ordeal we found ourselves suffering. After only about forty minutes, a shaft of light appeared at the end of the cramped space we were all crammed into. To me, the light signalled a beacon of hope and I allowed myself the luxury of feeling intense relief that we had been found.

Soon there was a hole big enough for us all to get through one at a time.

I made my way out of what could have been my final resting place and blinked in the afternoon sunlight. I looked around and did a quick mental count and realised that, out of the twenty workers standing in the shadow of the wall, only thirteen of us had been lucky enough to survive. I couldn't stop the tears running down my cheeks. I tried to rub them away but only succeeded in smearing them across my dirt covered face. I could only stand and watch as the broken bodies of my dead work mates were lifted gently out of the rubble.

I turned away from the awful scene, unable to watch anymore as I tried to imagine how sad the loved ones of the dead would be feeling. I turned to look at Susan just as she was returning Jane to her mother and, for a brief moment, both women held onto each other, fleetingly, brought together by their joint relief that Jane was alive.

I watched as Jane's grandmother placed the baby back into her pram and began to wheel her away. Susan looked wistfully after her, I had never seen a person look so lost and alone in my entire life and I wished things could have been different for her. I swiped the tears from my face once more; my sorrow was now replaced by anger.

This bloody war had a lot to answer to. How were we expected to behave when we were hundreds of miles away from our families and loved ones? Who could blame a person for seeking comfort from someone or something else? The amount of death and destruction was making me feel as though my life was spiralling out of control.

I wanted to scream and punch the wall and ask why? As I tried to get my emotions in check, I felt two sets of arms simultaneously embrace me. I looked around to see my dear friends standing either side of me. Susan, Joyce and I hugged each other tightly and then cried together for a minute.

Soon after, we all took deep breaths then linked each other's arms and walked towards our different homes. We all needed a good wash and something to eat then we arranged to meet later in the red Lion. I now had a middle aged lady living with me and I enjoyed the company but she would never be as close to me as Joyce and Susan, I loved them both with all my heart. Everything we had been through together had bought us closer together and I liked to believe that we had a bond that nothing could break.

I decided to rent out the uninhabited bedroom, in my house because I thought it unfair that I had an empty spare room when so many of Bristol's population were homeless. The lady, named Rita, who lodged with me, was a lovely woman who had lost all her family in a raid and we rubbed along together nicely. The arrangement was preferable to coming home to an empty house after a long, gruelling shift at the factory and the rent money came in handy.

That evening, as Joyce, Susan and I drank sweet Sherries in the pub, sitting at our regular table, it was obvious to me that we were all a little subdued and not our normal cheery selves. Our conversation did not flow as freely as it always did and I believed that we were all still in a state of shock. The government posters all told us how had to 'keep calm and carry on', 'our country needed us' and 'keep up the bulldog spirit'.

This was all true and we endeavoured to do this but sometimes the tragedies that happened were too much and we were only human and needed to allow ourselves a bit of time to wallow in our sadness, for one evening only. In the morning we would paint on a smile on our faces and work to win the war. For now, however, we would sit and thank God that we had survived to fight another day. I then sat back and envisaged what I would do when the war ended and I was reunited with my family once more.

Six weeks after Jane was born, Jimmy, Susan's boyfriend was posted back to Clifton in Bristol. He was lucky enough to meet his daughter on two occasions when he met up with Susan and her mother at the local Lyons tea shop. Sadly the happy arrangement didn't last long. When Jane was just three months old her grandmother was killed.

They were sheltering in the basement of their terraced house when it took a direct hit from a German shell. Susan's mother threw herself over Jane's body to save her and it cost the brave woman her life. Susan told me that she believed it was the ultimate thing her mother could do for her and how she could now find it in her heart to forgive her for the years they spent apart.

Susan decided to ask my sister-in-law, Lucy if she would adopt Jane. Bristol and the circumstances of Jane's birth made it too dangerous for her to remain with Susan. Lucy was absolutely overjoyed with the arrangement as she had no children of her own and longed for baby. Practically, it worked out brilliantly for all involved but on an emotional level it took its toll on Susan. I waved my tearful friend off, one wet and windy afternoon, on the day she took Jane to Ireland and bid her a final farewell and my heart broke for her.

30

March 10 1944
MICHAEL

I had now been fighting in the jungle for long that, in my mind, my previous life ceased to exist. All I knew was the here and now. Wenling and I had become lovers soon after Ruolan was killed. Wenling was not my type at all; I preferred petite, delicate figures, not someone who was the same height and build as me so I was unsure what the attraction was. I think our mutual love for Ruolan drew us to each other or maybe the fraught physical need to feel the touch of a fellow human body close by when we were was surrounded by death and carnage.

We often talked about Ruolan when we lay together; reminiscing about the happy times we shared with her. It helped us both to cope with our overwhelming feeling of loss and deep-rooted grief that happened when you lost a person who was very dear to you. At some point during the time I was fighting the guerrilla war and without my knowledge, American joined China in the fight against the Japanese. With no correspondence from the outside world and without any newspapers or radio, I remained convinced that China was fighting a solitary war of its own.

I think it must have been about early 1944, as I was leaning over the fire, attempting to blow some life into it when I heard a noise that was now alien to me and I was momentarily shocked. I took the safety off my pistol and checked my knife was in its holster before I rose cautiously and looked to where the sound was coming from. When, in the near distance, I spotted an unfamiliar uniform I immediately assumed it to be another enemy and I raised my rifle and fixed my bayonet, ready for immediate attack.

My eyes and mind were completely focused on the task ahead of me, which was to kill the approaching foe before it killed me; I switched off any doubts, regarding the unrecognisable uniform, and ran towards the danger. Through the black clouds that seemed to be puffing around inside my head, I was sure I thought I heard someone shout at me to stop. I concluded that it was a trap, designed to confuse me monetarily and then shoot me where I stood, then I heard it again, louder and more urgent this time:

'No buddy, calm down and lower your weapon, we're on your side!'

But it was too late for me; my time in the Burmese jungle had turned me into a soulless being that was used to murdering or maiming any unfamiliar person who came near me and who didn't speak Chinese. I launched myself at the enemy, only to find myself hopelessly out numbered. I was being attacked from all sides. I struggled for all my life was worth; I thrashed around wildly, searching for one of the many weapons I carried but all to no avail. I tried to screech my very own Chinese war cry but I found myself strangely mute.

I was afraid. The continuous struggle was beginning to weaken me but not my assailants; they seemed to be swarming across the area like a plague of greedy locusts. My fight became futile; I was outnumbered by a stronger fighting force with more advanced weapons. I felt an unexpected twinge of sadness that my life was about to end but also an eerie sense of relief that I would have to fight no more and that the killing was over.

I let myself go limp. I allowed the air to leave my body, like a deflated balloon, in preparation for death. Through the melee and tussle, a rush of emotion seemed to wash over me and I was overcome with a deep sense of release and calm. I thought I felt a quick but sharp pain in my forearm. I was instantly overcome with a feeling of 'not being in my own body'; it was as though I was watching what happened to me while I was floating above. It was a strange and terrifying sensation but I also felt a sense of freedom.

It was as though my body, which had been as taught and tight as a strongly coiled spring for such a long time, was now beginning to slowly uncoil. For the first time in many months I fell into a state of total relaxation. I allowed myself to fall further into this comatose state and permitted the overwhelming exhaustion that had plagued me for such s long time to fully encompass me and dropped into a deep, undisturbed sleep. Sometime later, I have no idea how long, I could hear voices and feel my body moving but I had no control or care about what was happening to me.

At one point I struggled to lift my heavy eyelids and managed to peer through the two slits I had made. I was being helped up by two men in uniform. My legs dragged along the floor, flapping around as though they were made of rubber. My helpless body was hoisted into a vehicle of some sort. There was nothing I can do. I was no longer the instigator of my own actions or my impending destiny. I imagined I was sitting on a moving cloud but there was no way I could get off, the softness of my seat was paralysing me.

I couldn't work out if the fear was worse than my usual constant fear, of being killed or having to kill someone, or if it was a new, jumbled kind of fear of the unknown and what faced me at the end of my journey.

The next sensation I could recall was the feel of the tide ebbing below me and I knew I was on a boat. I have no idea how much time had passed, it could have been minutes or it might have been days. My sight was still hazy when I opened my eyes, and I shook my head to try and focus.

The black blobs around me eventually materialised into shapes then the shapes turned into people. There were other men in the room with me. They were all injured. Some were horrifically burned and others had missing limbs or features. I could hear the groans of pain and the pleas for help. I could smell the stench of death and rotting carcasses mixed with stale blood and bodily fluids.

The gentle rocking of the ship was both calming and frightening at the same time. I wanted to run away from this place as fast as I could but I felt as though I was imprisoned in a lifeless body. I tried to open my lips to tell anyone who would listen that I needed to get out but no sound came from my mouth; it felt as though my voice has been silenced by an unknown force. I eventually allowed the darkness to engulf me once more. I was as helpless as a new born baby and I had no idea what to do.

At some point, during my semi consciousness, something penetrated deep into the realms of my awareness and I feel myself being strapped into a seat of some kind. I then heard the familiar sound of the engines of a ship sailing out to sea and I knew I was being taken away from China. I was pretty sure I was on my way back to Burma and I tried to mentally ready myself for the ordeal I was about to suffer but it was as though my brain has turned into a marshmallow. For some reason, even the sharp images of my evil Japanese captors did mot frighten me, and I couldn't work out why.

Time must have moved on because I came to feel as though I was trapped amongst a bleeding, seething mess of humanity. Was I on the way to hell or was I already there? I could now see that there were other people in the room; some of the other men were staring ahead but seemingly looking at nothing. Maybe, I wondered, were they studying the tiny specks of dust that danced around in the narrow shafts of light that the portholes allowed in, or maybe they could see something that I couldn't. Some of the wretched souls were so horribly burned I couldn't distinguish which part of their body I was looking at. These men were heavily swathed in bandages but eerily silent, seemingly oblivious to the agony they must be suffering.

I watched as one soldier lay on a stretcher, he was staring at the ceiling above him but looking at nothing, with his arms outstretched as though he was trying to grab hold of something that only his eyes can see. I lifted my own arm, it felt as heavy as a giant boulder so I let it drop into my lap once more and found myself physically exhausted by that one small effort.

I turned my head to my left and I could see the clouds out of a small port hole above me and I wanted to become one. I needed to float away into another land where wars and killing did not happen. In my head, it felt as though I had been skipping from one nightmare to another. I wanted it to stop. I wanted to be back in Ireland delivering groceries for the local shop, like I used to be doing but I didn't know when that was. I wanted to be flying down the lush Irish hills on my bike with the wind whipping my hair into a frenzy. I could almost feel the breeze caressing my face and making my eyes water.

A picture of a beautiful young woman's face came into my mind. She is petite with dark blonde hair and emerald green eyes. Her smile is so bright it lights up my mind. I know this is my wife, Lucy, but I'd forgotten all about her, how could I have done that? I have an almost painful longing to see her and hold her in my arms. I want to feel her soft hair rubbing against my cheeks and smell her lily-of-the-valley perfume. I think I am smiling as I see a flickering image of her dancing around our tiny kitchen, wearing a new summer frock. Lucy had always loved new clothes... I think.

As the ship cut through the choppy waves, other pictures flickered though my mind like a film on a cine camera. I can see the faces of a small, wide-eyed child and a dark haired oriental woman. Who are these people and what are their faces doing in my mind? The women's face disappears then reappears in the photo album in my mind but she is dead, her sightless eyes tell me that she no longer lives in this world. I struggle to remember but my brain feels like it is a lump of cotton wool. I don't know how long I was on the ship for but it seemed to go on forever.

Every time some sharpness came back into my mind, I felt the need to lash out, for my own safety and protection. Each time this happened I felt the sharp prick of an injection in my arm then peace and harmony would return to my life and I was content watch the sea float by through the small round window. I could never work out if I was in heaven or hell or if I was flitting between the two places. Finally the ship must have docked because the rocking movement ceased. I became aware that I was outside when I felt the breeze ruffle through my hair.

I tried to shake the haze from my mind and work out where I was. I felt myself being transported but had no idea how or by whom. I gazed through my tired eyes at the scenery around me. The land around me seemed familiar; I saw green grass and trees surrounded by fallen leaves. However, my mind couldn't seem make any sense of my whereabouts. Voices seemed to be sounding around me but I could not work out what they were saying.

I must have fallen asleep because when I woke I found myself in a small room, lying on a narrow, iron framed bed. There was a small window in the wall above me that did not allow much light to penetrate into the damp darkness. My head ached and my throat was dry and sore. I tried to pull myself into a sitting position but the effort was too much and I flopped back down onto spiky, feather-filled pillows. I wondered if I was in prison, this was how I imagined a prison cell would look. Eventually I heard open as it rubbed along the floor and I looked up to see it being pushed open by a uniformed man:

'Hello matey, welcome home, you're safe now' said the man with such a thick Scottish accent I barely understood him, I didn't believe him when he said I was safe:

'Where am I?' I croaked, because of the dryness of my throat. He looked down at me and the look on his face was filled with compassion and pity but I didn't know why and I didn't trust him:

'You're at the hospital mate and we'll take care of you, don't worry now, we're here to help.'

I heard the door shuffle open further. Another man, dressed in khaki coloured overalls walked in and put a tray of food on the small table in the corner of the room. He lifted the cloth that was covering it and my mouth literally began to water. On the tray was a roast dinner and some jam sponge pudding with custard, beside that was cup of tea.

I looked at the feast as though I was mesmerised. The first man who had entered the room picked up the tea and held it to my lips. I took a small sip of the warm, refreshing liquid; it tested like nectar and I gasped as it trickled down the back of my throat and soothed away all the dryness. I was then helped into a sitting position. Between them the two men helped me to eat and I savoured the joyous taste and texture of the wonderful feast I had been given. I think, at that point, I believed it was the most delicious meal I had ever eaten.

I felt monumentally better after my food although my body still felt as weak as a tiny kitten; my mind seemed a little more alert and less woozy and I began to take in my surroundings more carefully. I decided that I didn't think it was a prison because there were no bars on the small window and I wasn't chained to anything. I lay on my bed, feeling full for the first time in many years and I enjoyed the sensation and couldn't help smiling.

After a short rest the two men in uniform returned and heled me up into a sitting position once more and, eventually, out of the bed. I stood wobbling, like a small child who's just learned to walk. My limbs felt heavy and cumbersome. I shuffled along a narrow corridor, unable to walk unaided. I am guided towards a door with two panes of patterned glass at the top. It was pushed open and I was helped into what looked like a doctor's surgery.

I wanted to walk independently but it felt as though my legs were too weak and floppy to carry my weight. There was also an odd sensation in my head; it felt as though there was a bee buzzing around inside my skull. I staggered as my two helpers moved away from me and the man sitting at the desk, in the room, rushes forward to stop me from falling. He was wearing a pristine white coat that seems to shine. He slowly led me to a long couch alongside the back wall.

He helped me up onto the couch and told me to lie down. I did as I was told. It wouldn't do to agitate my captors. My time fighting had taught me that. Curiously, I was unable to keep still because my body twitched involuntarily and I couldn't stop it. I again, tried to talk but my words didn't sound right.

It was almost as though I was listening to a two year just learning to form sounds. The doctor began to speak and I listened to what he was saying. He was telling me that I was suffering from a post combat psychiatric disorder and that I was at a hospital in Scotland that would help me to get better.

I couldn't work out how I'd travelled to Scotland, had I been in some type of time machine that had transported me here in record time? I wanted to believe the man as he kept reassuring me that I was in a place of safety but all the time he talked I was looking around the room, readying myself for attack at any given moment. I didn't trust him, though I don't know why. My eyes were fixed on the door. I wanted to be rigid and taunt so that I was prepared for the enemy attack but my body refused to cooperate with my mind and continued to twitch.

My eyes shot around the room looking for a warning that danger was approaching. I turned back to the doctor and was petrified to see the Japanese guard who had tried to shoot me standing in his place. I screeched, a high pitched animal scream, and tried to get off the bed and run. I knew it was a trick! I had fallen for their lies after everything I had been though and now I was in enemy hands once more.

Even as I was looking at him the Jap soldier morphed back into the doctor in the white coat shocking me to the core, I believed there was strange phenomenon's occurring, designed to make me think I was insane. I wouldn't let them win. I tried to shake my head to clear my fuzzy mind; I couldn't understand what was happening and I was beginning to feel paralysed with fear.

The man leant over me and insisted to me, once more, that I was in a place of safety but I did not believe him. He had not seen what I had just seen. My body trembled as though an electric vault travelled up through it. The man was talking once more and he had a soothing voice but I thought that could just be because he was trying to trap me into trusting him but I was no fool.

A movement behind his left shoulder made my eyes swivel in that direction and there was my beautiful Roulan, she was holding my daughter, Truin. They were both smiling and I smiled back. I was so happy to be with my gorgeous little family once more but I also needed to protect them. Suddenly, blood began to spurt from Roulan's head. She did not cry out, she just fell to the ground. I tried to get to her but I couldn't move. Then they were gone, where they stood was just a blank wall and a tiny window, and the curtain was blowing in the breeze.

I began to shout and beg for help for myself and my family. It was all I could do. The doctor was shouting back at me, telling me to calm down. He wouldn't listen to what I was saying. From out of nowhere, I felt my strength rush back into my body and flow though my veins. I needed this man to understand the urgency of my situation and how important it was for me to get my wife and daughter to safety. I tried to shake him to penetrate through his seemingly unbreakable core.

The two men rushed back into the room. Again, I was outnumbered and being overpowered by the enemy. Now three Japanese guards were pinning me down with their full weight upon me and I could not breathe. I reached for my knife but it was not in my belt neither was my gun in its holster. The extreme terror I felt gave me a power that I didn't know I possessed. I thrust my body upwards and my three captors flew off me. I needed to escape. I crawled wildly then managed to drag myself to my feet and pull open the closed door.

I looked outside and stopped in my track. It was a complete hive of activity. The sun was burning down and now my throat ached with dryness due to the humidity and lack of water. All around me were half-starved men, who were barley skin and bone, feverishly working to build the railway. The Japs stood guard with their evil, hate-filled eyes boring into the backs of prisoners.

I quickly bent down to try to avoid looking at them and grabbed my pick axe. As long, as I avoided eye contact and worked until I dropped I would be safe. The sweat dripped down my face and into my eyes, stinging them, I ignored the pain. The Japanese guards turned to face, they then approached slowly and menacingly and I began to fight for my life.

I looked up again and I was in the hospital corridor. I shook my head sharply, I was unable to understand what was happening to me and I was very frightened. I was holding an umbrella in my hand but I had no idea where it had come from. Before I could work out what was happening, I felt myself being manhandled to the ground.

A jacket-like garment was being wrapped around me so I could no longer move my arms. I lay on the floor, my confusion felt palpable. Real life didn't seem to exist anymore. I felt as though I was trapped in some kind of nightmarish dream, nothing made sense.

The next thing I knew, I was being hoisted to my feet and I looked at the two men who were propelling me along. They were the same guys who had given me food and water earlier on in the day. Both of them now had bloodied noses and one had a badly bruised eye that was swelling bigger by the minute and was partially closed. I wondered what had happened to them and if they had been in a fight of some sort.

I was manhandled into a small room then thrown to the floor. It didn't hurt though because the room was soft and padded. I lay, panting with exhaustion but didn't know why. I only knew that someone was playing a sick joke on me and I needed to get away as soon as I could. I wanted to try and formulate an escape plan in my mind but I was finding it difficult because my mind didn't seem want help. It was as though any clear thoughts that filtered through quickly became distorted. To me, it felt like I was in semi-conscious state but, at the same time, I was aware of what was happening to me.

Time held no meaning for me; I had no idea if it was day or night. At some time I was released from the jacket that clamped my arms to my side but remained imprisoned in the cell. My arms ached when I moved them. At another point in the day, I don't know when, food was pushed through a flap in the door. I grabbed it quickly and threw the food hungrily down my throat. I needed to get my strength back if I was to continue fighting.

I decided my imprisonment was another Japanese form of torture. I guessed their idea was to isolate me from my fellow prisoners but I couldn't work out why. Maybe they had decided that I was a trouble maker but why not just kill me? That's what usually happened in the hellhole that was Burma. At some point in my captivity, I was taken to another small room. Three of my captors shackled me so tightly that even the smallest movement was impossible.

Tied tightly down onto a narrow bed, I was then injected with an unknown substance. It now felt as though I had actually moved out of my body and was one of the dust particles floating above because I felt so light, as though I didn't weigh an ounce. The atoms were swirling and dancing when they got caught in a small prism of light coming through the tiny, square window.

I heard a voice, coming from somewhere in the distance:

'Where do you think you are Michael old chap?' It was in a childlike voice, as though someone thought I was a small boy and he was trying to pacify me.

'Burma sir, I'm working on the railway, I can't stop, and if I do they will kill me.' I avoided eye contact as I spoke:

'Michael, you are in Scotland, in the hospital, we're here to help you,' the calming voice persisted.

'No sir, that's not possible, I can feel the heat of the sun on my face and I've heard the Jap guards, they are wandering the corridors tapping their bayonet on the door and screeching out orders, can't you hear them too?'

I was taken back to another room in a haze of wonderment and confusion. I have no idea how many of these calming sessions I attended but at some point, along the way, I actually began to believe the calm voice that spoke to me. I became aware of important things that backed up the man's story.

I slowly realised that where I was now didn't smell like Burma but it smelt of disinfectant and sometimes I caught the odour of food cooking. Not on a campfire but the smells that permeated from a working kitchen. There was no such smell in Burma because rice being boiled had no odour.

As the meetings continued, my mind began to clear, as though something was brushing away the cobwebs and allowing me to see through. It felt as if I was hacking through a thatch of brambles and moving them out the way. As they did so my thinking became more and more rational.

At some point, I was no longer tethered or guarded. I was moved into a long room with several other men. Some stared into space at nothing at all although their eyes were steadily focused. Others screamed out and begged for mercy but I couldn't see what was distressing them. As I slowly began to feel, a little saner, the rest of the inmates became, in my mind, like deranged creatures. I longed to be out of this place before I became as insane as them.

After a long period of time, I have no idea how long, I came to realise that I was in a hospital. I was told that I had suffered a breakdown of some kind and my mind had been affected. It took me several months to finally realise where I was and to try and work out what had happened to me. I was well on the way to recovery in every aspect of my life, apart from one small thing. I didn't know who I was.

I questioned the doctor about this, at my next session; he explained that it was totally natural for the mind to do this when it had suffered such inner turmoil it could no longer cope. It was a kind of closing down mechanism and form of protection. The medic suggested hypnosis to help me remember. At that point, I was happy to try anything. I found it a very unpleasant sensation to look myself in the mirror and see a total stranger looking back.

I was very nervous about starting my first session but also quite excited. I wanted to know who I was and if this was the only way to find out, I must just get on and do it. I entered a sterile room. The only furniture it contained was two single chairs in the centre facing each other. There was a man, whom I assumed was a doctor because of his white coat, seated in one of the chairs and he motioned for me to sit on the other.

I did as I was told. The man looked straight into my eyes and began to speak. I didn't feel as if I had been hypnotised but, as time went on, the doctor's voice began to sound as though it was coming from a distance. I was overcome with an emotion of serenity and peace:

'What's your name old chap?' he enquired. I thought for a moment and suddenly my mind was as clear as a sunlit day:

'My name is Jian,' I answered confidently and felt a sense of relief sweep over me.

'Where do you live?' the monotone voice continued,

'I am based deep in the jungle in China with my wife Roulan and my daughter, Truin. We are a united army fighting for China's freedom', I finished proudly.

I smiled, in my mind I could see Truin's cheeky little face grinning up at me and Roulan's broad smile as she tickled our little girl's soft tummy. The image was abruptly shattered and then it disappeared like a cloud of smoke:

'Your name is Michael Rosenthal, your wife is Lucy and you have a young daughter called Jane.' The voice said.

The clearness of my mind disappeared once more and was replaced by a murky, grey swamp. I protested but the voice insisted several times over, ignoring what I was saying and growing louder in volume and intensity. I sat through several of these sessions, and as time progressed I began to dread them more and more.

I found myself making excused not to attend but I was physically manhandled to the meetings. To me, it felt as though the voice was bullying me and trying to turn me into someone I wasn't. I cannot recall how many of these treatments I had or for how long I was treated. I only remember one particular day. It was as though a light bulb had suddenly become illuminated in the centre of my brain.

I know that it was around the middle of June because the sun was shining brightly in a beautiful, blue, cloudless sky. I could hear larks tweeting their tunes and I could perceive the faint screech of seagulls in the far distance. Previous to this session I had been reading a book, while sitting in the grounds of the hospital. The warming sunshine was caressing my face and a small breeze was whistling through my hair.

I looked up into the clear azure sky and it was as if someone had flipped a switch in my mind. As I gazed into the blueness above, an image of Lucy's face appeared in the shape of a cloud. She was smiling and pointing at me. I stood up and gazed skywards until the image faded then I rushed back into the building to find my doctor. This time I begged for another sitting.

I raced towards his consulting room and banged on the door. He shouted for me to come and I walked breathlessly into the room towards him, exhausted by my sudden sprint to locate him. We sat facing each other on the two chairs and he began to speak. I smiled widely and said:

'My name is Michael Rosenthal; formerly Maciej and I originate from Germany. I am a German Jew and my brother, Levin and I fled our native country many years ago, my wife is Lucy and she adopted a baby girl, named Jane, while I was a prisoner of war,' I gabbled, in rush to get the words out before I forgot them once more.

I didn't realised I had closed my eyes but I must have done because when I opened them I saw the doctor grinning widely at me. He leant forward and shook my hand heartily. He then opened his drawer and took out a bottle of whisky and poured a glug each into a couple of glasses then handed me one:

'Welcome back old chap,' he beamed, 'you made a wonderful sacrifice for England and fought for its freedom, I am honoured to have brought you back.' We clinked glasses and I too was now grinning from ear to ear. We both finished our drinks and I returned to the garden once more. I lay down on the warm grass and put my hands behind my head. All in a rush, memories poured into my mind.

I pictured Gerta in her kitchen insisting I eat a meal she made. I smiled as the grass prickled the back of my neck. As the days passed more recollections returned. I remembered my brother Leonard and his wife Violet. I was ecstatic to recall that I was a much loved member of a family and it felt as though my life was coming back together again. I asked if I would be allowed to write to Lucy and the doctor wholeheartedly assured me that I could. As time went by my mind began to heal a little more each day and I started to imagine a life outside the hospital and began to put the horrors of war firmly in the past where they belonged.

I was out in the grounds one glorious day, enjoying the sunshine, when I was informed that I had a visitor. The sun was high in the sky and fluffy white clouds hung lazily above me. It was always a relief to be outside and not in the sanitary building that had been my home for such a long time. The sun was scorching hot.

The heat on my back comforted me as I prepared myself for whoever my visitor was. I remember thinking it may be a member of the clergy, they often visited us men once we were on the mend. I believe it was to renew our faith in whatever religion we had formerly practised.

I sat waiting patiently then I put my hand above my eyes to shield them from the sun. It was then that I saw the apparition walking towards me. Her golden, shining hair was partially covered by a straw hat, tied at the neck with a red ribbon. She wore a white dress decorated with bright red poppies and white sandals. I thought I was hallucinating as I rose, slowly, from my chair. I walked, cautiously, hardly able to believe what I was seeing, towards the beacon of normality and then she began to run towards me.

I ran towards her and pulled her into my arms. I clung onto my beautiful wife, Lucy and realised that she was no apparition but an actual flesh and blood person. The smell of her melted away all my troublesome thoughts and I held onto her tightly as she whispered how much she loved me. We both sat on the fresh grass; I held onto her soft hand and gazed into her wonderful, laughing eyes.

I drank in every single part of her. Still I was unable to believe that she was actually here and not something I had dreamt up. At first, we were a little awkward in each other's company; we had been apart for a very long me. After a short while, however, the awkwardness began to disintegrate into the fresh morning air and we started talked as we used to before the war tore us apart. The years we were separated melted away.

When Lucy told me that she had brought our daughter Jane with her, I instantly wanted to meet the little girl. Lucy smiled excitedly then waved to a couple some distance away and they began to walk towards us. I looked up to see my brother Len and his wife Violet walking towards me. Toddling between them, holding a tiny hand each was a little girl.

She had a heart shaped face and dark blonde hair tied in pigtails with two yellow ribbons. As the came closer I stood up and watched, proudly as she took her faltering steps on her own. I then dropped to my knees introduced myself to my daughter.

She smiled a wide beaming smile that warmed the cavities of my heart then immediately pointed to her shoes and told me that they were her best ones. I told her they were lovely, as was she, and she grinned at me once more. It felt as though a gateway had opened in my existence and this was what I was born for.

In my mind, this little girl was the beacon of hope for my future. She and Lucy would be the beloved people that I would strive to protect at all times. All I had ever wanted, since I fled

Germany with Leonard, was a loving home and family and now I had one. In the future, when I was deemed well enough to return home to Ireland with Jane and Lucy I vowed that I would do everything I could to make them happy. I finally wanted to stop the enduring ripples of war and float in a mill-pond of joy.

THE END